"HYMNAL SUPPLEMENT II"

Agape

AGAPE
Carol Stream, Illinois 60188

Carlton R. Young, Executive Editor
Austin C. Lovelace, Editor
Jane Marshall, Editor
W. Thomas Smith, Editor

Contributors

Alan Cowle
Carol Doran
Carol Giesbrecht
Gracia Grindal
David Hurd
David C. Isele
Joy Lawrence
Robin A. Leaver
Alice Parker
Richard Proulx
Russell Schulz-Widmar
James R. Sydnor
Thomas H. Troeger
Jaroslav Vajda
John Wilson

FOREWORD

HYMNAL SUPPLEMENT II represents hymn singing practices and tastes of a broad spectrum of the English speaking world. Limited to new expressions of praise from the past fifteen years (either text or tune or both), the editors have carefully examined a vast resource pool of material submitted by fifteen distinguished contributors from Great Britain and North America.

British hymn singing preferences were represented by Guildford's John Wilson and Robin Leaver, presently on the faculty of the Westminster Choir College in Princeton, New Jersey. Canadian interests were advanced by Alan Cowle of Toronto and Carol Giesbrecht of Kitchener. Carol Doran and Tom Troeger from Colgate Rochester Divinity School shared their views with Gracia Grindal of Luther Northwestern Theological Seminary in St. Paul. Also represented was David Hurd, Professor of Church Music and Organist of The General Theological Seminary in New York City. David Isele from the University of Tampa and Joy Lawrence from University Heights, Ohio, added a fresh perspective. Composer Alice Parker from New York City and Director of Music and Organist Richard Proulx from Holy Name Cathedral in Chicago contributed to the broadened framework. Church Musician and Scholar Russell Schulz-Widmar from Austin, Texas, and Hymnologist James Sydnor from Richmond, Virginia, also enriched the resources. Lutheran Editor/Scholar Jaroslav Vajda completed the group of contributors whose input was invaluable.

Directing the project was the working editorial team who met on a number of occasions over a two-year span. Headed by Executive Editor Carlton R. Young, who is presently serving as editor of the revision of the Methodist Hymnal, the editorial team was comprised of composer/teacher Jane Marshall of Dallas, Texas; organist/conductor/hymnologist Austin C. Lovelace of Denver, Colorado; and The Hymn Society of America's Executive Director, W. Thomas Smith of Fort Worth, Texas.

HYMNAL SUPPLEMENT II is dedicated to Fred Pratt Green, who two decades ago initiated the "hymnic explosion" in Great Britain, which has now become a "hymnal explosion" here in the United States.

> And did not Jesus sing a Psalm that night
> When utmost evil strove against the Light?
> Then let us sing, for whom he won the fight:
> Alleluia!
>
> Fred Pratt Green

THE PUBLISHERS

This Is the Threefold Truth

1

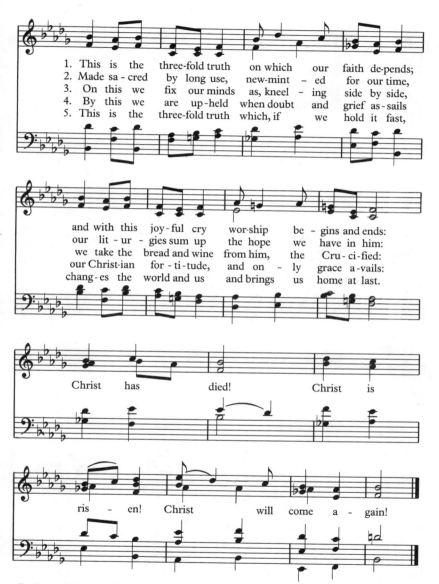

Two features of this setting provide a musical representation of the "threefold truth." The syncopated rhythm occurs thrice, each time accompanied by parallelism in the tenor and bass voices. The note cluster g♭ - a♭ - b♭ also occurs thrice: once in each of the three main parts of the acclamation, "Christ has died! Christ is risen! Christ will come again!"

WORDS: Fred Pratt Green
MUSIC: William P. Rowan

THREEFOLD TRUTH
66.66.12.

Let All the World

Let all the world in ev - ery cor - ner

sing: my God and King!

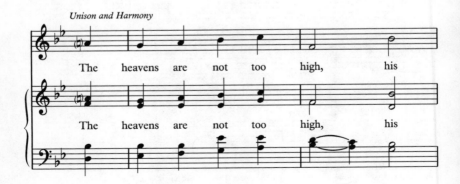

The heavens are not too high, his

The heavens are not too high, his

praise may thith - er fly; the earth is not too

low, his prais-es there may grow. Let all the

Unison

Org.

world in ev - ery cor - ner

sing: my God and King!

Harmony

2. The church with psalms must shout, no

door can keep them out; but a - bove all, the

heart must bear the long-est part. Let all the

heart must bear the long-est part.

world in ev-ery cor-ner

sing: my God and King!

WORDS: George Herbert
MUSIC: Erik Routley

AUGUSTINE
66.66. with Antiphon

Music Copyright © 1976 by Hinshaw Music, Inc. Reprinted by permission.

3   Creating God, Your Fingers Trace

Unison

1. Cre - a - ting God, your fin - gers trace the
2. Sus - tain - ing God, your hands up - hold earth's
3. Re - deem - ing God, your arms em - brace all
4. In - dwell - ing God, your gos - pel claims one

bold de - signs of far - thest space; let sun and moon and
mys - t'ries known or yet un - told; let wa - ter's fra - gile
now de - spised for creed or race; let peace des - cend - ing
fam - ily with a bil - lion names; let ev - ery life be

stars and light and what lies hid - den praise your might.
blend with air, en - a - bling life, pro - claim your care.
like a dove, make known on earth your heal - ing love.
touched by grace un - til we praise you face to face.

WORDS: Jeffery Rowthorn
MUSIC: Pilsbury's *United States Harmony*, 1799

KEDRON
LM

Eternal Light

4

1. E - ter - nal light, shine in my heart; e - ter - nal hope, lift up my eyes; e - ter - nal power, be my sup - port; e - ter - nal wis - dom, make me wise.
2. E - ter - nal life, raise me from death; e - ter - nal bright - ness, help me see; e - ter - nal Spir - it, give me breath; e - ter - nal Sav - ior, come to me:
3. Un - til by your most cost - ly grace, in - vit - ed by your ho - ly word, at last I come be - fore your face to know you, my e - ter - nal God.

WORDS: Christopher Idle; from a prayer by Alcuin
MUSIC: Jane Marshall
JACOB
LM

5

As a Chalice Cast of Gold

1. As a chal - ice cast of gold,
2. Save me from the sooth - ing sin
3. When I bend up - on my knees,
4. When I dance or chant your praise,

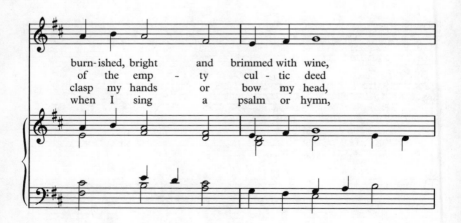

burn-ished, bright and brimmed with wine,
of the emp - ty cul - tic deed
clasp my hands or bow my head,
when I sing a psalm or hymn,

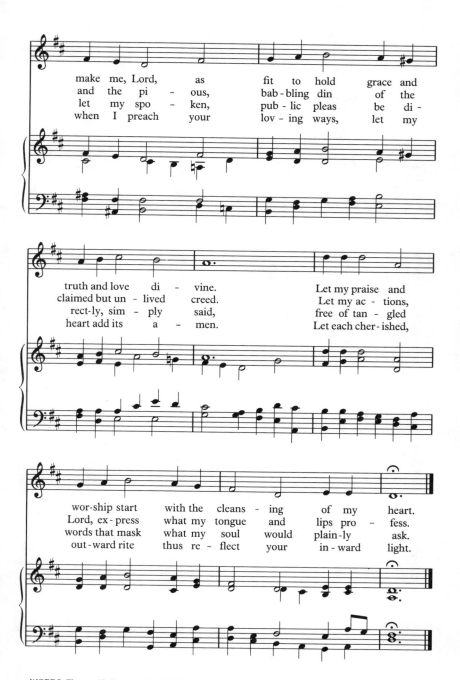

WORDS: Thomas H. Troeger, Mark 7:1-8, 14-15, 21-23
MUSIC: Carol Doran

INWARD LIGHT
77.77.77.

6

Christ, Mighty Savior

1. Christ, might - y Sav - ior, Light of all cre -
2. Now comes the day's end as the sun is
3. There- fore we come now eve - ning rites to
4. Give heed, we pray you, to our sup - pli -
5. Though bod - ies slum - ber, hearts shall keep their

a - tion, you make the day - time
set - ting: mir - ror of day - break,
of - fer, joy - ful - ly chant - ing
ca - tion: that you may grant us
vig - il, for ev - er rest - ing

ra - diant with the sun - light and to the
pledge of res - ur - rec - tion; while in the
ho - ly hymns to praise you, with all cre -
par - don for of - fens - es, strength for our
in the peace of Je - sus, in light or

night give glit - ter - ing a - dorn - ment,
heav - ens, choirs of stars ap - pear - ing
a - tion join - ing hearts and voic - es
weak hearts, rest for ach - ing bod - ies,
dark - ness wor - ship - ing our Sav - ior

stars in the heav - ens.
hal - low the night - fall.
sing - ing your glo - ry.
sooth - ing the wea - ry.
now and for ev - er.

WORDS: Mozarabic Rite, 10th cent.; tr. Alan G. McDougall; rev. Anne K. LeCroy   MIGHTY SAVIOR
MUSIC: David Hurd   11 11 11.5.

7

Amid the World's Bleak Wilderness

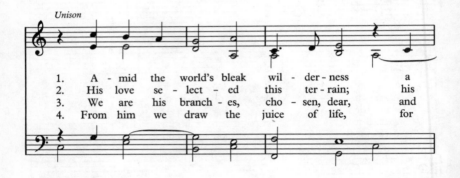

1. A - mid the world's bleak wil - der - ness a
2. His love se - lect - ed this ter - rain; his
3. We are his branch - es, cho - sen, dear, and
4. From him we draw the juice of life, for

vine - yard grows with prom - ise green, the
vine with love he plant - ed here to
though we feel the dress - er's knife, we
him sup - ply his win - er - y with

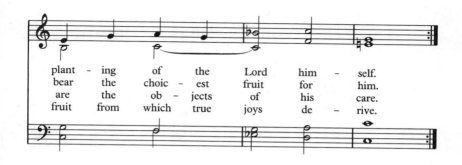

plant - ing   of   the   Lord   him -   self.
bear   the   choic - est   fruit   for   him.
are   the   ob -   jects   of   his   care.
fruit   from   which   true   joys   de   –   rive.

5. Vine, keep what   I   was   meant   to   be: your

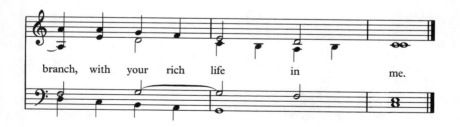

branch, with   your   rich   life   in   me.

WORDS: Jaroslav J. Vajda
MUSIC: Richard W. Hillert

GRANTON
Irregular

8

Christ Is Risen! Shout Hosanna!

Unison

1. Christ is ris – en! Shout Ho - san – na!
2. Christ is ris – en! Raise your spir – its
3. Christ is ris – en! Earth and heav – en

Cel – e - brate this day of days!
from the cav – erns of des – pair.
nev - er - more shall be the same.

Christ is ris – en! Hush in won – der:
Walk with glad – ness in the morn - ing.
Break the bread of new cre - a – tion

all cre - a - tion is a - mazed.
See what love can do and dare.
where the world is still in pain.

From Gol - goth - a's doom con - found - ing,
Drink the wine of res - ur - rect - ion,
Tell its grim, de - mon - ic chor - us:

see a spread - ing tree has grown. Heal-ing leaves of
not a ser - vant, but a friend, Je - sus is our
'Christ is ris - en! Get you gone!' God the First and

grace a-bound-ing bring a taste of love un - known.
strong com-pan-ion. Joy and peace shall ne - ver end.
Last is with us. Sing Ho-san - na ev - ery - one!

WORDS: Brian Wren
MUSIC: William P. Rowan

JACKSON NEW
87. 87. D.

Copyright © 1986 by Hope Publishing Company, Carol Stream, IL 60188. All Rights Reserved.

9

Christ the Lord Has Risen

(A war song gathered at Garu in the Upper Region of Ghana. Must be sung fast, preferably with rolling drum beat accompanying the people's parts. The words by Tom Colvin turn a traditional war song into a Christian victory song.)

Leader   *All*

2. Sin has done its worst, sin has done its worst,
4. He is Lord of Lords, he is Lord of Lords,
6. All the world is his, all the world is his,
8. Christ our Lord, has ris'n, Christ our Lord has ris'n,

yes, Lord.   Sin has done its worst,
Je - su.   He is Lord of Lords,
Je - su.   All the world is His,
Je - su.   Christ our Lord, has ris'n.

sin has done its worst, yes, Lord.
he is Lord of Lords, Je - su.
all the world is his, Je - su.
Christ our Lord has ris'n, Je - su.

WORDS: Tom Colvin
MUSIC: Northern Ghana Folk Song, adpt. by Tom Colvin

GHANA
Irregular

10 Come, Risen Lord

1. Come, ris - en Lord, and deign to be our guest;
nay, let us be thy guests: the feast is thine;
thy - self at thine own board made man - i - fest,
in thine own sac - ra - ment of bread and wine.

2. We meet, as in that up - per room they met;
thou at the ta - ble bles - sing, yet dost stand;
'this is my bo - dy:' so thou giv - est yet:
faith still re - ceives the cup as from thy hand.

3. One bo - dy we, one bo - dy who par - take,
one Church u - ni - ted in com - mu - nion blest;
one name we bear, one bread of life we break,
with all thy saints on earth and saints at rest.

4. One with each o - ther, Lord, for one in thee,
who art one Sa - vior and one liv - ing Head;
then o - pen thou our eyes, that we may see;
be known to us in break-ing of the bread.

WORDS: George W. Briggs
MUSIC: Cyril V. Taylor

BOROUGH
10 10. 10 10.

At the Lamb's High Feast 11

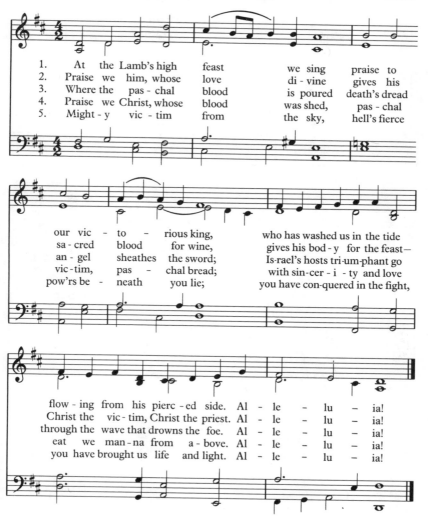

1. At the Lamb's high feast we sing praise to
2. Praise we him, whose love di - vine gives his
3. Where the pas - chal blood is poured death's dread
4. Praise we Christ, whose blood was shed, pas - chal
5. Might - y vic - tim from the sky, hell's fierce

our vic - to - rious king, who has washed us in the tide
sa - cred blood for wine, gives his bod - y for the feast—
an - gel sheathes the sword; Is-rael's hosts tri-um-phant go
vic - tim, pas - chal bread; with sin-cer - i - ty and love
pow'rs be - neath you lie; you have con-quered in the fight,

flow - ing from his pierc - ed side. Al - le - lu - ia!
Christ the vic - tim, Christ the priest. Al - le - lu - ia!
through the wave that drowns the foe. Al - le - lu - ia!
eat we man - na from a - bove. Al - le - lu - ia!
you have brought us life and light. Al - le - lu - ia!

6. Now no more can death appall,
   now no more the grave enthrall;
   you have opened paradise,
   and your saints in you shall rise.
   Alleluia!

7. Easter triumph, Easter joy!
   This alone can sin destroy;
   from sin's pow'r, Lord, set us free,
   newborn souls in you to be.
   Alleluia!

8. Father, who the crown shall give,
   Savior, by whose death we live,
   Spirit, guide through all our days:
   Three in One, your name we praise.
   Alleluia!

WORDS: Office hymn, 17th cent; tr. Robert Campbell
MUSIC: Bohemian Brethren, *Kirchengesang*, 1566

SONNE DER GERECHTIGKEIT
77.77.4.

12   Be Known To Us

1. Be known to us in break - ing bread, but
2. There sup with us in love di - vine; thy

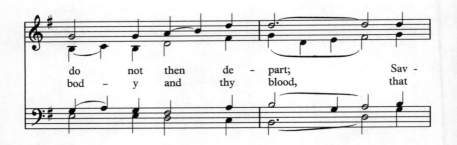

do not then de - part; Sav -
bod - y and thy blood, that

ior,   a - bide   with   us,   and   spread   thy
liv - ing   bread,   that   heav'n - ly   wine,   be

ta - ble   in   our   heart.
our   im - mor - tal   food.

Organ (ad lib.)

espressivo

Senza Ped.

rall.

Ped.

WORDS: James Montgomery
MUSIC: Traditional melody, arr: John Wilson

LAND OF REST
CM

13

Glorious the Day

1. Glo - rious the day when Christ was born to
2. Glo - rious the day when Christ a - rose, the
3. Glo - rious the day of Gos - pel grace when
4. Glo - rious the day when Christ ful - fills what

wear the crown that Cae-sars scorn,
sur - est friend of all his foes; Al - le - lu - ia! Al - le -
Christ re-stores the fall - en race,
self re-jects yet feeb - ly wills;

lu - ia! Al - le - lu - ia! Al - le - lu - ia!

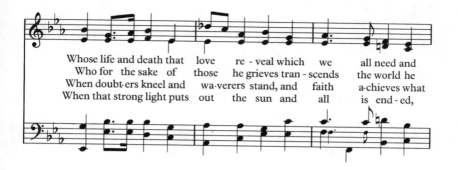

Whose life and death that love re - veal which we all need and
Who for the sake of those he grieves tran - scends the world he
When doubt-ers kneel and wa-verers stand, and faith a-chieves what
When that strong light puts out the sun and all is end - ed,

need to feel:
nev - er leaves; Al - le - lu - ia! Al - le -
rea - son planned;
all be - gun;

lu - ia! Al - le - lu - ia! Al - le - lu - ia!

WORDS: Fred Pratt Green
MUSIC: William P. Rowan

PLOGER
88.88. with Alleluia

14

Glory to God in the Highest

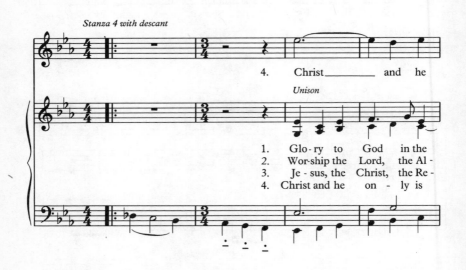

Stanza 4 with descant

4. Christ_____ and he

Unison

1. Glo-ry to God in the
2. Wor-ship the Lord, the Al -
3. Je-sus, the Christ, the Re -
4. Christ and he on - ly is

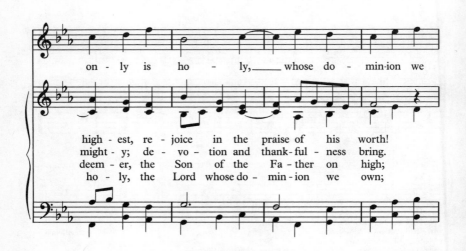

on - ly is ho - ly,___ whose do - min-ion we

high - est, re - joice in the praise of his worth!
might - y; de - vo - tion and thank-ful - ness bring.
deem - er, the Son of the Fa - ther on high;
ho - ly, the Lord whose do - min - ion we own;

own;   one with the   Fa-ther,   one with the

Glo-ry   to   God   in the high-est, all   crea-tures of
'Praise be to   God   for his   glo-ry and   peace to   his
led as   a   Lamb   to the slaugh-ter, the   Lord who was
one with the   Fa - ther and Spir-it, most   high, ev - er -

Spir-it reign - ing in glo   -   ry,   the   glo -

heav-en-ly birth!   Glo-ry to   God   in the high-est, and
peo-ple,' we sing;   'Glo-ry to   God   in the high-est, the
will-ing to   die;   God in the   heav - en-ly plac-es, 'Have
last-ing, a - lone;   reign-ing e - ter - nal in   glo-ry, the

- ry of   God on   his   throne.   A -   men.

peace to his   peo-ple   on   earth!
Fa-ther and   heav-en-ly   King.'
mer-cy up - on us,' we   cry.
glo-ry of   God on   his   throne.   A -   men.

WORDS: Timothy Dudley-Smith
MUSIC: Richard Proulx

RUSSWIN
88.88.88.

15

Open Are the Gifts of God

1. O - pen are the gifts of God, gifts of love to mind and sense; hid - den is love's ag - o - ny, love's en - deav - or, love's ex - pense.
2. Love that gives, gives ev - er - more, gives with zeal, with ea - ger hands, spares not, keeps not, all out - pours, ven - tures all, its all ex - pands.
3. Drained is love in mak - ing full, bound in set - ting oth - ers free, poor in mak - ing man - y rich, weak in giv - ing power to be.
4. There - fore he who shows us God help - less hangs up - on the tree; and the nails and crown of thorns tell of what God's love must be.
5. Here is God: no mon - arch he, throned in eas - y state to reign; here is God, whose arms of love, ach - ing, spent, the world sus - tain.

WORDS: W. H. Vanstone
MUSIC: Adapt. from Orlando Gibbons

SONG 13
77. 77.

Of All the Spirit's Gifts to Me   16

Unison

1. Of all the Spir-it's gifts to me, I
2. He shows me love is at the root of
3. He shows me that if I pos-sess a
4. Though what's a-head is mys-ter-y, and
5. We go in peace but made a-ware that

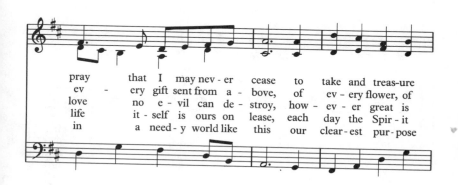

pray that I may nev-er cease to take and treas-ure
ev-ery gift sent from a-bove, of ev-ery flower, of
love no e-vil can de-stroy, how-ev-er great is
life it-self is ours on lease, each day the Spir-it
in a need-y world like this our clear-est pur-pose

most these three: love, joy and peace.
ev-ery fruit, that God is love.
my dis-tress, that this is joy.
says to me: go forth in peace.
is to share love, joy and peace.

WORDS: Fred Pratt Green
MUSIC: Austin C. Lovelace

THREEFOLD GIFTS
888. 4.

17

Praise the Lord!

Unison

Praise the Lord! Praise, O ser-vants of the Lord! Praise the
Praise the Lord! Thanks and prais-es sing to God! Day by
Praise the Lord! Praise and glo - ry give to God! Who is
Praise the Lord! Praise, O ser-vants of the Lord! Praise the

name of the Lord! Bless-ed be the name of the Lord!
day to the Lord! High a - bove the na-tions is God,
like un - to him? Rais-ing up the poor from the dust,
love of the Lord! Giv-ing to the home-less a home,

Bless-ed be the name of the Lord from this time
high a - bove the na-tions is God, his glo - ry
rais - ing up the poor from the dust, he makes them
giv - ing to the home-less a home, he fills their

forth and for - ev - er – more! Praise the Lord! Praise the Lord!
high o-ver earth and sky! Praise the Lord! Praise the Lord!
dwell in his heart and home. Praise the Lord! Praise the Lord!
hearts with new hope and joy! Praise the Lord! Praise the Lord!

WORDS: Marjorie Jillson. Psalm 113:1, 2, 4
MUSIC: Heinz Werner Zimmermann

CARPENTER
Irregular

Rise, Shine, You People! 18

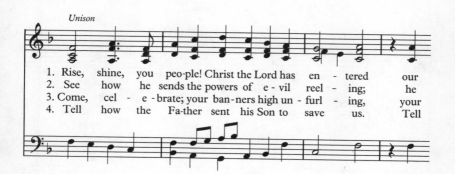

1. Rise, shine, you peo-ple! Christ the Lord has en - tered our
2. See how he sends the powers of e - vil reel - ing; he
3. Come, cel - e -brate; your ban-ners high un - furl - ing, your
4. Tell how the Fa-ther sent his Son to save us. Tell

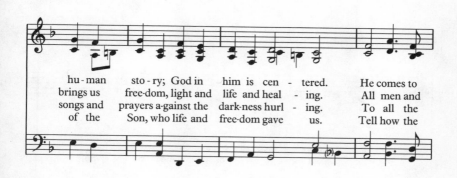

hu - man sto - ry; God in him is cen - tered. He comes to
brings us free-dom, light and life and heal - ing. All men and
songs and prayers a-gainst the dark-ness hurl - ing. To all the
of the Son, who life and free-dom gave us. Tell how the

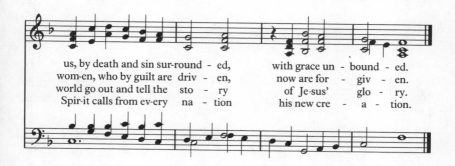

us, by death and sin sur-round - ed, with grace un - bound - ed.
wom-en, who by guilt are driv - en, now are for - giv - en.
world go out and tell the sto - ry of Je-sus' glo - ry.
Spir-it calls from ev-ery na - tion his new cre - a - tion.

WORDS: Ronald A. Klug. Isaiah 60:1
MUSIC: Dale Wood

WOJTKIEWIECZ
11 11 11.5.

19

God Is Here!

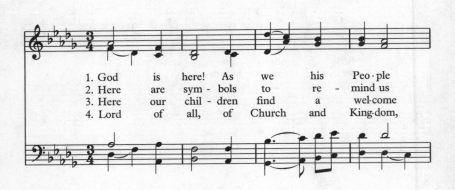

1. God is here! As we his Peo-ple
2. Here are sym - bols to re - mind us
3. Here our chil - dren find a wel-come
4. Lord of all, of Church and King-dom,

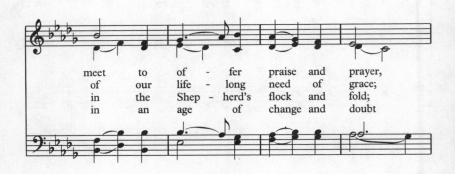

meet to of - fer praise and prayer,
of our life - long need of grace;
in the Shep - herd's flock and fold;
in an age of change and doubt

may we find in full - er meas - ure
here are ta - ble, font and pul - pit;
here, as bread and wine are tak - en
keep us faith - ful to the gos - pel,

what it is in Christ we share. Here, as
here the cross has cen-tral place. Here, in
Christ sus-tains us as of old. Here, the
help us work your pur-pose out. Here, in

in the world a-round us, all our var-ied
hon-es-ty of preach-ing, here in si-lence,
ser-vants of the Ser-vant seek in wor-ship
this day's ded-i-ca-tion, all we have to

skills and arts wait the com-ing of the
as in speech, here, in new-ness and re-
to ex-plore what it means in dai-ly
give, re-ceive: we, who can-not live with-

Spir-it in-to o-pen minds and hearts.
new-al, God the Spir-it comes to each.
liv-ing to be-lieve and to a-dore.
out you, we a-dore you! We be-lieve!

WORDS: Fred Pratt Green
MUSIC: Cyril V. Taylor

ABBOT'S LEIGH
87.87.D.

20 Blessed Be the God of Israel

Unison

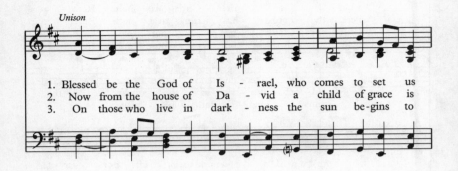

1. Blessed be the God of Is - rael, who comes to set us
2. Now from the house of Da – vid a child of grace is
3. On those who live in dark - ness the sun be - gins to

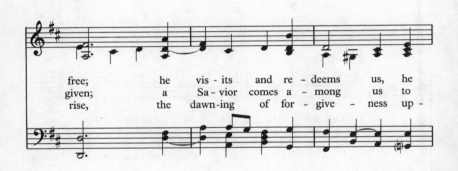

free; he vis - its and re - deems us, he
given; a Sa - vior comes a - mong us to
rise, the dawn-ing of for - give - ness up-

grants us lib – er - ty. The pro - phets spoke of
raise us up to heaven. Be - fore him goes his
on the sin - ner's eyes. It guides the feet of

mer	-	cy,	of	free	-	dom and	re	-	lease;	God
her	-	ald,	fore-run - ner	in	the	way,	the
pil	-	grims a - long	the	paths	of	peace.	O

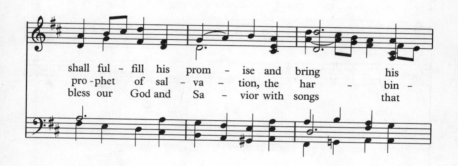

shall ful - fill his prom - ise and bring his
pro -phet of sal - va - tion, the har - bin -
bless our God and Sa - vior with songs that

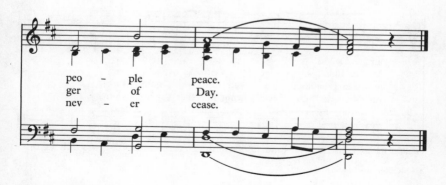

peo - ple peace.
ger of Day.
nev - er cease.

WORDS: Michael A. Perry
MUSIC: Basil Harwood

THORNBURY
76. 76. D.

Come, Let Us Eat

21

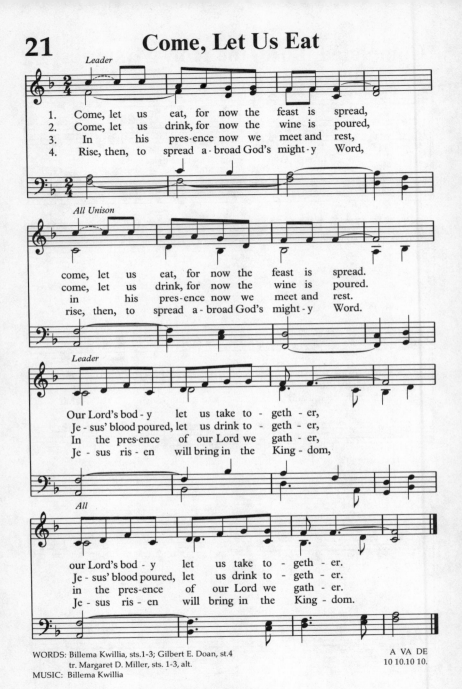

Leader

1. Come, let us eat, for now the feast is spread,
2. Come, let us drink, for now the wine is poured,
3. In his pres-ence now we meet and rest,
4. Rise, then, to spread a-broad God's might-y Word,

All Unison

come, let us eat, for now the feast is spread.
come, let us drink, for now the wine is poured.
in his pres-ence now we meet and rest.
rise, then, to spread a-broad God's might-y Word.

Leader

Our Lord's bod-y let us take to-geth-er,
Je-sus' blood poured, let us drink to-geth-er,
In the pres-ence of our Lord we gath-er,
Je-sus ris-en will bring in the King-dom,

All

our Lord's bod-y let us take to-geth-er.
Je-sus' blood poured, let us drink to-geth-er.
in the pres-ence of our Lord we gath-er.
Je-sus ris-en will bring in the King-dom.

WORDS: Billema Kwillia, sts.1-3; Gilbert E. Doan, st.4
tr. Margaret D. Miller, sts. 1-3, alt.
MUSIC: Billema Kwillia

A VA DE
10 10.10 10.

Completed, Lord, the Holy Mysteries 22

1. Com - ple - ted, Lord, the Ho - ly Mys-ter-ies, as far as lies with - in our mor-tal power! Thy death re-mem-bered feed-ing thus on thee, we here have known the res - ur - rec - tion hour.

2. Here we have tast - ed in - fi - nite de - lights, be - held a - far that life which soon shall be; Oh, count us wor-thy, Christ, thy joys to share, for - ev - er in e - ter - ni - ty with thee.

3. Through God's good grace these Mys-ter - ies are ours, or - dained by thee, the ev - er-last-ing Son; blest by the Spi-rit, breath and flame of life, to whom be praise while end-less ag - es run.

WORDS: Liturgy of St. Basil, tr. Cyril E. Pocknee
MUSIC: David Hurd

ROBERTSON
10 10.10 10.

23 Jesus, Come! For We Invite You

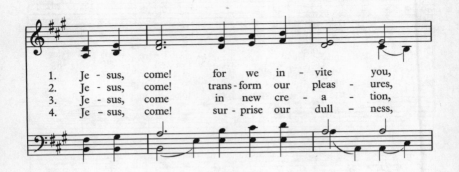

1. Je - sus, come! for we in - vite you,
2. Je - sus, come! trans - form our pleas - ures,
3. Je - sus, come in new cre - a - tion,
4. Je - sus, come! sur - prise our dull - ness,

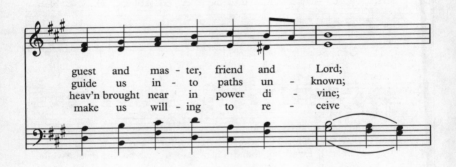

guest and mas - ter, friend and Lord;
guide us in - to paths un - known;
heav'n brought near in power di - vine;
make us will - ing to re - ceive

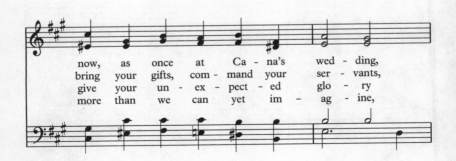

now, as once at Ca - na's wed - ding,
bring your gifts, com - mand your ser - vants,
give your un - ex - pect - ed glo - ry
more than we can yet im - ag - ine,

speak, and let us hear your word:
let us trust in you a - lone:
chang - ing wa - ter in - to wine:
all the best you have to give:

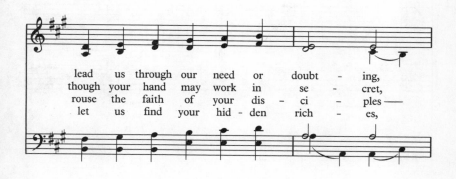

lead us through our need or doubt - ing,
though your hand may work in se - cret,
rouse the faith of your dis - ci - ples —
let us find your hid - den rich - es,

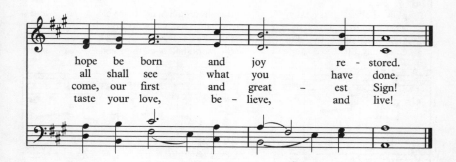

hope be born and joy re - stored.
all shall see what you have done.
come, our first and great - est Sign!
taste your love, be - lieve, and live!

WORDS: Christopher Idle, John 2   BEST GIFT
MUSIC: Ronald F. Krisman   87. 87. 87.

A Stable Lamp Is Lighted

1. A sta - ble lamp is light - ed whose
2. (This) child through Da-vid's ci - ty shall
3. (Yet) he shall be for - sak - en, and
4. (But) now, as at the end - ing, the

glow shall wake the sky; the stars shall bend their voic - es, and
ride in tri - umph by; the palm shall strew its branch - es, and
yield - ed up to die; the sky shall groan and dark - en, and
low is lift - ed high; the stars shall bend their voic - es, and

2. This
3. Yet
4. But

WORDS: Richard Wilbur
MUSIC: David Hurd

ANDUJAR
76.76.66.76.

God Said

Unison

1. God said, "A star will rise, and in the
2. God said, "A rose will bloom; green leaves ap-
3. God said, "A lamb will come, will-ing to
4. God said, "Be-hold my Son: he is your

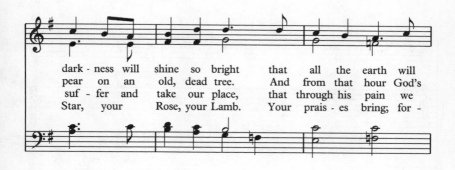

dark - ness will shine so bright that all the earth will
pear on an old, dead tree. And from that hour God's
suf - fer and take our place, that through his pain we
Star, your Rose, your Lamb. Your prais - es bring; for -

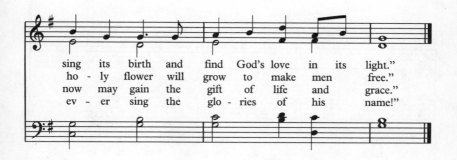

sing its birth and find God's love in its light."
ho - ly flower will grow to make men free."
now may gain the gift of life and grace."
ev - er sing the glo - ries of his name!"

WORDS and MUSIC: Frederick John Steffen

GOD SAID
69.44.6.

26 Before the Marvel of This Night

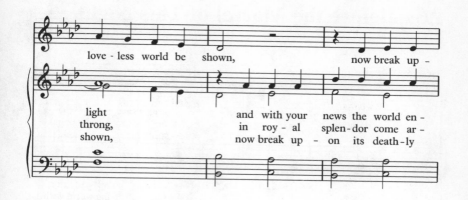

love-less world be shown,   now break up -

light   and with your   news the world en -
throng,   in roy - al   splen-dor come ar -
shown,   now break up - on its death-ly

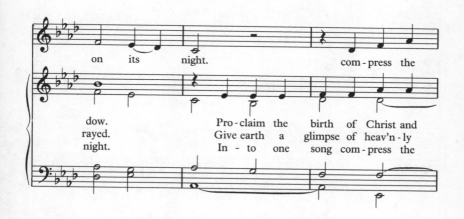

on   its   night.   com - press the

dow.   Pro - claim the   birth of Christ and
rayed.   Give earth a   glimpse of heav'n - ly
night.   In - to one   song com - press the

love   that   rules   our   un - i - verse a -

peace,   that fear and   death and sor - row
bliss,   a teas - ing   taste of what they
love   that rules our   un - i - verse a -

WORDS: Jaroslav J. Vajda
MUSIC: Carl Schalk

MARVEL
Irregular

When the King Shall Come Again 27

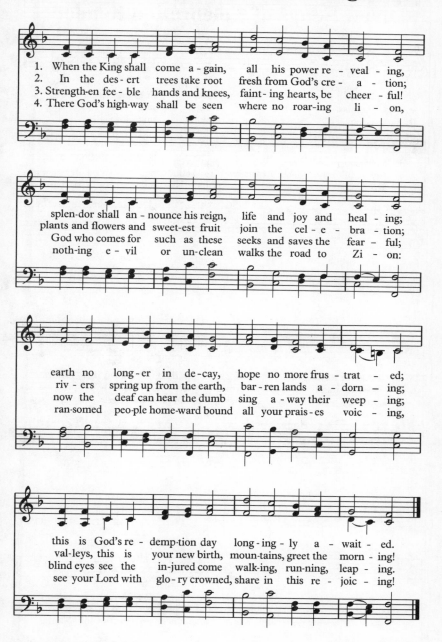

1. When the King shall come a-gain, all his power re - veal - ing,
2. In the des - ert trees take root fresh from God's cre - a - tion;
3. Strength-en fee - ble hands and knees, faint - ing hearts, be cheer - ful!
4. There God's high-way shall be seen where no roar-ing li - on,

splen-dor shall an - nounce his reign, life and joy and heal - ing;
plants and flowers and sweet-est fruit join the cel - e - bra - tion;
God who comes for such as these seeks and saves the fear - ful;
noth-ing e - vil or un-clean walks the road to Zi - on:

earth no long - er in de-cay, hope no more frus - trat - ed;
riv - ers spring up from the earth, bar - ren lands a - dorn - ing;
now the deaf can hear the dumb sing a - way their weep - ing;
ran-somed peo-ple home-ward bound all your prais-es voic - ing,

this is God's re - demp-tion day long - ing - ly a - wait - ed.
val-leys, this is your new birth, moun-tains, greet the morn - ing!
blind eyes see the in-jured come walk-ing, run-ning, leap - ing.
see your Lord with glo - ry crowned, share in this re - joic - ing!

WORDS: Isa. 35; Christopher Idle
MUSIC: Johann Horn

GAUDEAMUS PARITER
76. 76. D.

28
New Songs of Celebration Render

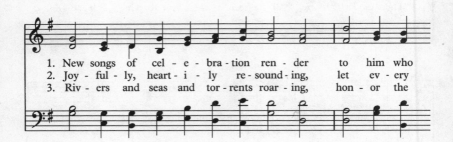

1. New songs of cel - e - bra - tion ren - der to him who
2. Joy - ful - ly, heart - i - ly re - sound - ing, let ev - ery
3. Riv - ers and seas and tor - rents roar - ing, hon - or the

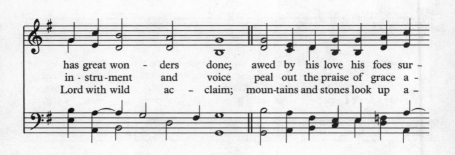

has great won - ders done; awed by his love his foes sur -
in - stru - ment and voice peal out the praise of grace a -
Lord with wild ac - claim; moun - tains and stones look up a -

ren - der and fall be - fore the Might- y One.
bound - ing, call - ing the whole world to re - joice.
dor - ing and find a voice to praise his Name.

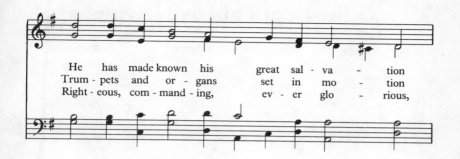

He has made known his   great sal - va - tion
Trum - pets and or - gans   set in mo - tion
Right - eous, com - mand - ing,   ev - er glo - rious,

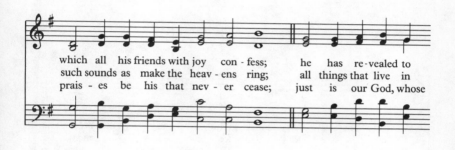

which all his friends with joy con - fess;   he has re - vealed to
such sounds as make the heav - ens ring;   all things that live in
prais - es be his that nev - er cease;   just is our God, whose

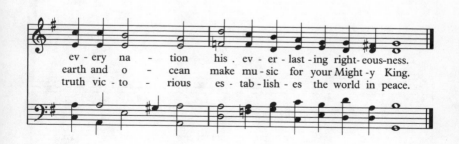

ev - ery na - tion his . ev - er - last - ing right - eous - ness.
earth and o - cean make mu - sic for your Might - y King.
truth vic - to - rious es - tab - lish - es the world in peace.

WORDS: Psalm 98, adapt. Erik Routley
MUSIC: Melody from *Genevan Psalter*, 1551, harm. by Erik Routley

RENDEZ À DIEU
98.98.D.

29   O the Depth of Love Divine

♩. = c. 60
Unison

1. O   the   depth   of   love   di - vine,   the   un -
2. Let   the   wis - est   mor - tal   show   how
3. How   can   heav'n - ly   spir - its   rise,   by
4. Sure   and   real   is   the   grace   the

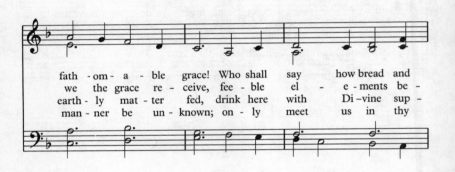

fath - om - a - ble   grace!   Who shall   say   how bread and
we   the grace   re - ceive,   fee - ble   el - e - ments be -
earth - ly   mat - ter   fed,   drink here   with   Di - vine sup -
man - ner   be   un - known;   on - ly   meet   us   in   thy

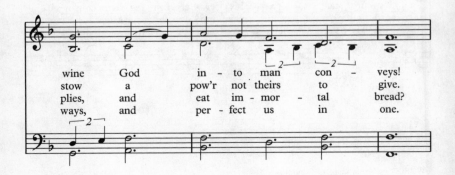

wine   God   in - to   man   con - veys!
stow   a   pow'r   not theirs   to   give.
plies,   and   eat   im - mor - tal   bread?
ways,   and   per - fect   us   in   one.

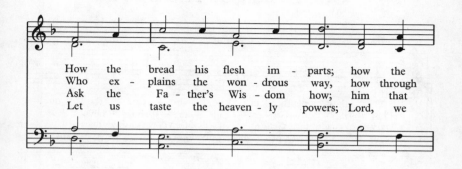

How the bread his flesh im - parts; how the
Who ex - plains the won - drous way, how through
Ask the Fa - ther's Wis - dom how; him that
Let us taste the heaven - ly powers; Lord, we

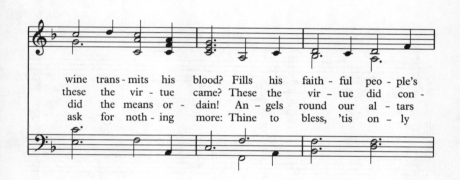

wine trans - mits his blood? Fills his faith - ful peo - ple's
these the vir - tue came? These the vir - tue did con -
did the means or - dain! An - gels round our al - tars
ask for noth - ing more: Thine to bless, 'tis on - ly

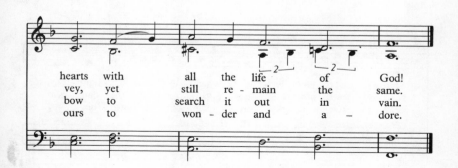

hearts with all the life of God!
vey, yet still re - main the same.
bow to search it out in vain.
ours to won - der and a - dore.

WORDS: Charles Wesley
MUSIC: Carlton R. Young

STOOKEY
76. 76. 77. 76.

30

God Sends Us His Spirit

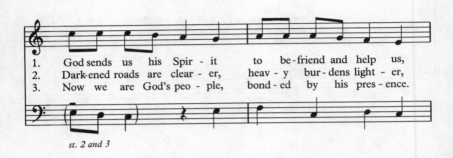

1. God sends us his Spir - it   to be - friend and help us,
2. Dark - ened roads are clear - er,   heav - y bur - dens light - er,
3. Now we are God's peo - ple,   bond - ed by his pres - ence.

st. 2 and 3

re - cre - ate and guide us,   Spir - it - Friend.
when we're walk - ing with our   Spir - it - Friend.
a - gents of his pur - pose,   Spir - it - Friend.

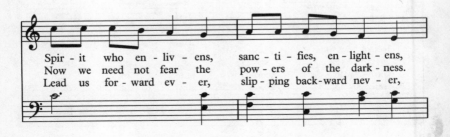

Spir - it who en - liv - ens,   sanc - ti - fies, en - light - ens,
Now we need not fear the   pow - ers of the dark - ness.
Lead us for - ward ev - er,   slip - ping back - ward nev - er,

(The words were written for those churches, particularly new ones, where the Spirit is experienced as a powerful presence. The traditional Gonja song was collected at Damongo by Tom Colvin aided by Rev. Natomah, the first Gonja to become a minister — one who loves his own tribe's traditions. Must be sung joyously and fast, preferably to drums and shakers. In the chorus, each "Spirit-Friend" should be accompanied by three sharp claps.)

Sets us free, is now our Spir - it - Friend.
None can o - ver - come our Spir - it - Friend.
To your re - made world, our Spir - it - Friend.

Refrain

hand claps

Spir - it of our Fa - ther, Spir - it - Friend.
Spir - it of our Je - su, Spir - it - Friend.

Spir - it of God's peo - ple, Spir - it - Friend.

WORDS: Tom Colvin
MUSIC: Gonja Folk Song

NATOMAH
12 9.12 9
with Refrain

31   On the Day of Resurrection

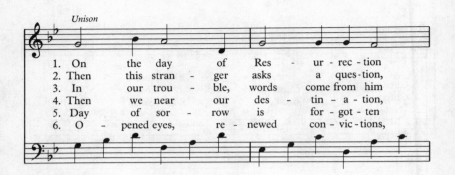

Unison

1. On the day of Res - ur - rec - tion
2. Then this stran - ger asks a ques - tion,
3. In our trou - ble, words come from him
4. Then we near our des - tin - a - tion,
5. Day of sor - row is for - got - ten
6. O - pened eyes, re - newed con - vic - tions,

to Em-ma - us we re -turn;   while con-fused, a-
"What is this which trou - bles you?"   Meets us in our
burn - ing fire with - in our hearts.   Tells to us the
then we ask the stran - ger in.   And he yields un -
when the guest be - comes the host.   Tak - ing bread and
jour - ney back to scene of pain,   tell - ing all that

mazed and fright-ened   Je – sus comes to us, un-known.
pain and suf-fering;   Je – sus walks with us, un-known.
scrip - ture's mean-ing,   Je – sus speaks to us, un-known.
to our urg-ing,   Je – sus stays with us, un-known.
bless - ing, break-ing,   Je – sus is him - self, made known.
Christ is ris - en: Je – sus is through us made known.

WORDS: Michael Peterson; Lk. 24:13-35
MUSIC: Mark Sedio

EMMAUS
87.87.

Christ Is Alive!

32

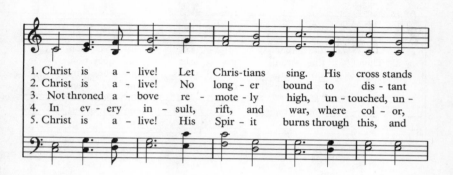

1. Christ is a - live! Let Chris-tians sing. His cross stands
2. Christ is a - live! No long - er bound to dis - tant
3. Not throned a - bove re - mote - ly high, un - touched, un -
4. In ev - ery in - sult, rift, and war, where col - or,
5. Christ is a - live! His Spir - it burns through this, and

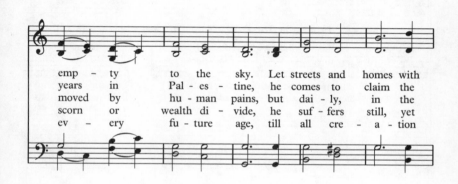

emp — ty to the sky. Let streets and homes with
years in Pal - es - tine, he comes to claim the
moved by hu - man pains, but dai - ly, in the
scorn or wealth di - vide, he suf - fers still, yet
ev — ery fu - ture age, till all cre - a - tion

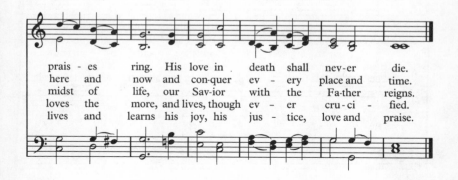

prais - es ring. His love in death shall nev-er die.
here and now and con-quer ev - ery place and time.
midst of life, our Sav-ior with the Fa-ther reigns.
loves the more, and lives, though ev - er cru-ci - fied.
lives and learns his joy, his jus - tice, love and praise.

WORDS: Brian Wren
MUSIC: Thomas Williams, *Psalmodia Evangelica*, 1789

TRURO
LM

Now the Silence

Now the si-lence Now the peace Now the emp-ty hands up-

lift-ed Now the kneel-ing Now the plea Now the Fa-ther's

arms in wel-come Now the hear-ing Now the power

Now the ves-sel brimmed for pour-ing Now the bod-y

Now the blood Now the joy - ful cel – e - bra - tion

Now the wed-ding Now the songs Now the heart for-giv – en leap-ing

Now the Spir-it's vis - i - ta - tion, Now the Son's e - piph - a - ny,

Now the Fa - ther's bless - ing Now Now Now

WORDS: Jaroslav J. Vajda
MUSIC: Carl F. Schalk

NOW
Irregular

34 Christ Is the World's Light

Unison

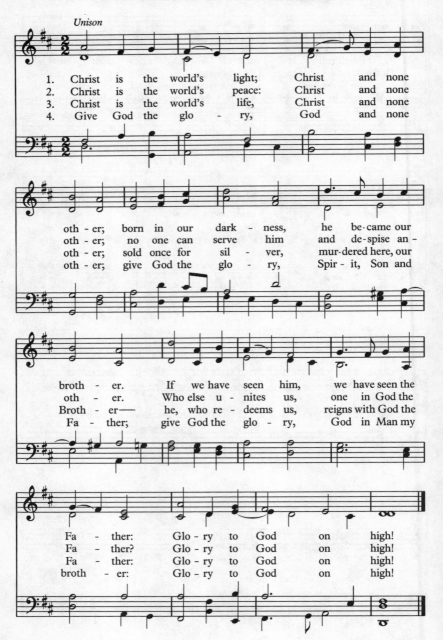

1. Christ is the world's light; Christ and none oth - er; born in our dark - ness, he be-came our broth - er. If we have seen him, we have seen the Fa - ther: Glo-ry to God on high!

2. Christ is the world's peace: Christ and none oth - er; no one can serve him and de-spise an - oth - er. Who else u - nites us, one in God the Fa - ther? Glo-ry to God on high!

3. Christ is the world's life, Christ and none oth - er; sold once for sil - ver, mur-dered here, our Broth - er— he, who re - deems us, reigns with God the Fa - ther: Glo-ry to God on high!

4. Give God the glo - ry, God and none oth - er; give God the glo - ry, Spir - it, Son and Fa - ther; give God the glo - ry, God in Man my broth - er: Glo-ry to God on high!

WORDS: Fred Pratt Green
MUSIC: French Church Melody, *Antiphoner*, Paris, 1681

CHRISTE SANCTORUM
10 11 11.6.

Up Through Endless Ranks of Angels

1. Up through end - less ranks of an - gels, cries of tri - umph
2. Death-de - stroy - ing, life - re - stor - ing, prov - en e - qual
3. To our lives of wan - ton wan-dering send your prom - ised
4. Al - le - lu - ia! Al - le - lu - ia! Oh, to breathe the

in his ears, to his heaven - ly throne as - cend - ing,
to our need, now for us be - fore the Fa - ther
Spir - it - Guide; through our lives of fear and fail - ure
Spir - it's grace! Al - le - lu - ia! Al - le - lu - ia!

hav - ing van-quished all their fears, Christ looks down up -
as our broth - er in - ter - cede; flesh that for our
with your power and love a - bide; wel - come us, as
Oh, to see the Fa - ther's face! Al - le - lu - ia!

on his faith - ful, leav - ing them in hap - py tears.
world was wound-ed, liv - ing, for the wound-ed plead.
you were wel-comed, to an end - less Eas - ter - tide.
Al - le - lu - ia! Oh, to feel the Son's em - brace!

WORDS: Jaroslav J. Vajda
MUSIC: Henry V. Gerike

ASCENDED TRIUMPH
87. 87. 87.

36 Lift High the Cross

Refrain Unison

Lift high the cross, the love of Christ pro - claim

till all the world a - dore his sa - cred name.

Harmony

1. As Mo - ses lift - ed up the bra - zen sign
2. Gaze at the Prince of Glo - ry hang-ing there
3. See there the crown of thorns, his wound-ed head,
4. We share the seal of wa - ter on our brow;
5. So let us fol - low in the glo-rious train

Refrain

so must we lift the rose of Jes - se's line:
who bears our sins too much for us to bear:
how for our lives his blood is free - ly shed:
the death of death is ours to fath-om now:
and sing with joy our song of life a - gain:

WORDS: Refrain by George W. Kitchin and Michael R. Newbolt
       Verses by Gracia Grindal
MUSIC: Sydney H. Nicholson

CRUCIFER
10 10.10 10.

Nature with Open Volume Stands 37

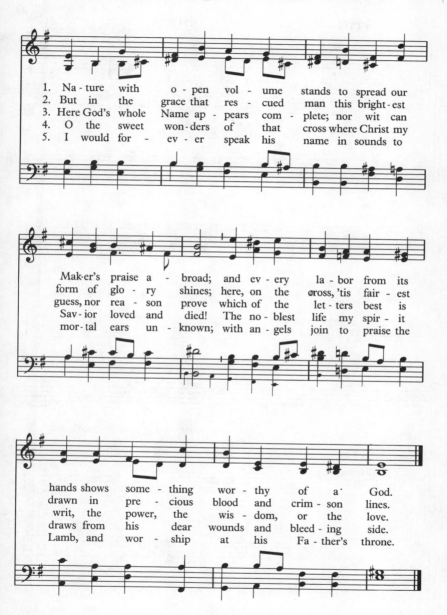

1. Na-ture with o-pen vol - ume stands to spread our Mak-er's praise a - broad; and ev - ery la - bor from its hands shows some - thing wor - thy of a God.
2. But in the grace that res - cued man this bright-est form of glo - ry shines; here, on the cross, 'tis fair - est drawn in pre - cious blood and crim - son lines.
3. Here God's whole Name ap - pears com - plete; nor wit can guess, nor rea - son prove which of the let - ters best is writ, the power, the wis - dom, or the love.
4. O the sweet won-ders of that cross where Christ my Sav - ior loved and died! The no - blest life my spir - it draws from his dear wounds and bleed - ing side.
5. I would for - ev - er speak his name in sounds to mor-tal ears un - known; with an - gels join to praise the Lamb, and wor - ship at his Fa - ther's throne.

WORDS: Isaac Watts
MUSIC: Mel. Nathaniel Gawthorn, harm. Samuel S. Wesley, ed. Erik Routley

ELTHAM
LM

38 God of the Sparrow

Woe
Care
Joy

How does the
How does the

crea – ture cry Save
crea – ture say Life

How do your chil – dren say Home

molto rit.

WORDS: Jaroslav J. Vajda
MUSIC: Carl Schalk

ROEDER
546.77.

Faith, While Trees Are Still in Blossom 39

Unison

1. Faith while trees are still in blos - som,
2. Long be - fore the dawn is break - ing,
3. Long be - fore the rains were com - ing,
4. Faith, up - lift - ed, tamed the wa - ter
5. Faith, be - lieves that God is faith - ful,

plans the pick - ing of the fruit; faith can feel the
faith an - ti - ci - pates the sun. Faith is eag - er
No - ah went and built an ark. A - bra - ham, the
of the un - di - vid - ed sea and the peo - ple
He will be who He will be. Faith ac - cepts His

thrill of har - vest, when the buds be - gin to sprout.
for the day - light, for the work that must be done.
lone - ly mi - grant, saw the Light be - yond the dark.
of the He - brews found the path that made them free.
call res - pond - ing: "I am will - ing; Lord, send me."

WORDS: Anders Frostenson, tr. Fred Kaan
MUSIC: *Southern Harmony*, 1835; arr. Carlton Young
Words Copyright by Ansgar Film & Bokproduktion. Used by permission.
Trans. Copyright © 1976 by Hope Publishing Company, Carol Stream, IL 60188.
Arrangement Copyright © 1982 by Hope Publishing Company. All Rights Reserved.

RESTORATION
8 7.8 7.

40 God, Whose Giving Knows No Ending

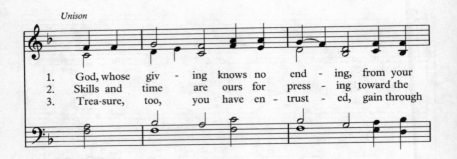

Unison

1. God, whose giv - ing knows no end - ing, from your
2. Skills and time are ours for press - ing toward the
3. Trea-sure, too, you have en - trust - ed, gain through

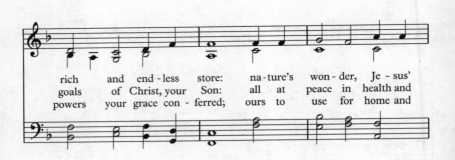

rich and end - less store: na - ture's won - der, Je - sus'
goals of Christ, your Son: all at peace in health and
powers your grace con - ferred; ours to use for home and

wis - dom, cost - ly cross, grave's shat - tered door,
free - dom, rac - es joined, the Church made one.
kin - dred, and to spread the Gos - pel Word.

gift - ed by you, we turn to you, of - fering
Now di – rect our dai - ly la - bor, lest we
O – pen wide our hands, in shar - ing, as we

up our - selves in praise; thank-ful song shall rise for -
strive for self a - lone: born with tal –ents, make us
heed Christ's age - less call, heal-ing, teach-ing, and re -

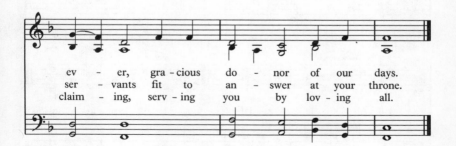

ev - er, gra - cious do - nor of our days.
ser - vants fit to an - swer at your throne.
claim – ing, serv - ing you by lov - ing all.

WORDS: Robert L. Edwards
MUSIC: *The Sacred Harp*, 1844; harm., James H. Wood

BEACH SPRING
87.87.D.

41 When in Our Music God Is Glorified

Unison

1. When in our mu - sic God is glo - ri -fied,
2. How of -ten, mak - ing mu - sic, we have found
3. So has the Church, in lit - ur - gy and song,
4. And did not Je - sus sing a Psalm that night
5. Let ev - ery in - stru -ment be tuned for praise!

and ad - o - ra - tion leaves no room for pride,
a new di - men - sion in the world of sound,
in faith and love, through cen - tu - ries of wrong,
when ut -most e - vil strove a - gainst the Light?
Let all re - joice who have a voice to raise!

it is as though the whole cre - a -tion cried
as wor -ship moved us to a more pro-found
borne wit - ness to the truth in ev - ery tongue,
Then let us sing, for whom he won the fight:
And may God give us faith to sing al - ways

1-4.
1-4. Al - le - lu - ia!

5.
5. Al - le - lu - ia!

WORDS: Fred Pratt Green
MUSIC: Charles V. Stanford

ENGELBERG
10 10 10. with Alleluia.

Filled with the Spirit's Power

42

1. Filled with the Spir-it's pow'r, with one ac-cord
2. Now with the mind of Christ set us on fire,
3. Wid-en our love, good Spir-it, to em-brace

the in-fant Church con-fessed its ris-en Lord.
that u-ni-ty may be our great de-sire.
in your strong care all those of ev-ery race.

O Ho-ly Spir-it, in the Church to-day
Give joy and peace; give faith to hear your call,
Like wind and fire with life a-mong us move,

no less your pow'r of fel-low-ship dis-play.
and read-i-ness in each to work for all.
till we are known as Christ's, and Chris-tians prove.

WORDS: John R. Peacey
MUSIC: Cyril V. Taylor

SHELDONIAN
10 10.10 10.

43

You Satisfy the Hungry Heart

You sat - is - fy the hun - gry heart with

gift of fin - est wheat; come give to us, O

sav - ing Lord, the bread of life to eat.

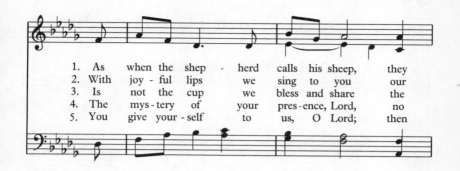

1. As when the shep - herd calls his sheep, they
2. With joy - ful lips we sing to you our
3. Is not the cup we bless and share the
4. The mys - tery of your pres - ence, Lord, no
5. You give your - self to us, O Lord; then

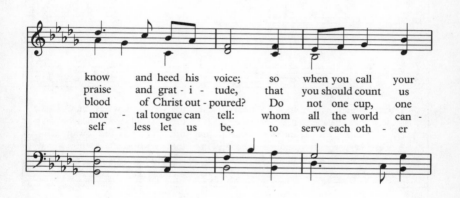

know and heed his voice; so when you call your
praise and grat - i - tude, that you should count us
blood of Christ out - poured? Do not one cup, one
mor - tal tongue can tell: whom all the world can -
self - less let us be, to serve each oth - er

fam - ily, Lord, we fol - low and re - joice.
wor - thy, Lord, to share this heaven - ly food.
loaf, de - clare our one - ness in the Lord?
not con - tain comes in our hearts to dwell.
in your name in truth and char - i - ty.

WORDS: Omer Westendorf
MUSIC: Robert E. Kreutz

FINEST WHEAT
CMD with Refrain.

44

For the Bread, Which Thou Hast Broken

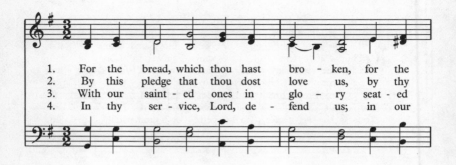

1. For the bread, which thou hast bro - ken, for the
2. By this pledge that thou dost love us, by thy
3. With our saint - ed ones in glo - ry seat - ed
4. In thy ser - vice, Lord, de - fend us; in our

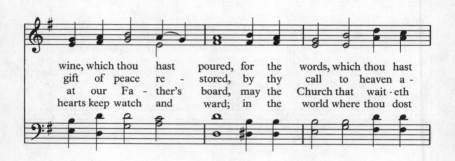

wine, which thou hast poured, for the words, which thou hast
gift of peace re - stored, by thy call to heaven a -
at our Fa - ther's board, may the Church that wait - eth
hearts keep watch and ward; in the world where thou dost

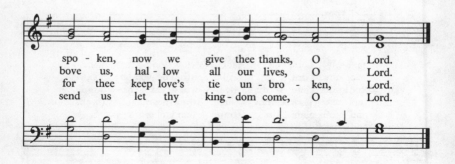

spo - ken, now we give thee thanks, O Lord.
bove us, hal - low all our lives, O Lord.
for thee keep love's tie un - bro - ken, O Lord.
send us let thy king - dom come, O Lord.

WORDS: Louis F. Benson
MUSIC: V. Earle Copes

KINGDOM
87.87.

Words used by permission of Robert F. Jefferys, Jr.
Music Copyright Renewal © 1987 by Abingdon Press. From THE BOOK OF HYMNS (#314). Used by Permission.

I Come with Joy

45

1. I come with joy to meet my Lord, for-giv-en,
2. I come with Chris-tians far and near to find, as
3. As Christ breaks bread and bids us share, each proud di-
4. And thus with joy we meet our Lord. His pres-ence,
5. To-geth-er met, to-geth-er bound, we'll go our

loved and free, in awe and won-der to re-call his
all are fed, the new com-mun-i-ty of love in
vi-sion ends. The love that made us, makes us one, and
al-ways near, is in such friend-ship bet-ter known; we
dif-ferent ways, and as his peo-ple in the world, we'll

life laid down for me, his life laid down for me.
Christ's com-mun-ion bread, in Christ's com-mun-ion bread.
stran-gers now are friends, and stran-gers now are friends.
see and praise him here, we see and praise him here.
live and speak his praise, we'll live and speak his praise.

WORDS: Brian Wren
MUSIC: American Folk Tune, arr. Austin C. Lovelace

DOVE OF PEACE
CM

46

Lord of the Boundless Curves of Space

1. Lord of the bound - less curves of
2. Your mind con - ceived the gal - ax -
3. Your Spir - it gave the liv - ing
4. Pri - me - val seeds of con - scious -
5. In Christ the liv - ing power of
6. Lead us, whom love has made and

space and time's deep mys - ter - y: to
y, each a - tom's se - cret planned, and
cell its hid - den, vi - tal force: the
ness, by grace have greened and grown to
grace to lib - er - ate and lead lights
sought, to find, when plan - ets fall, that

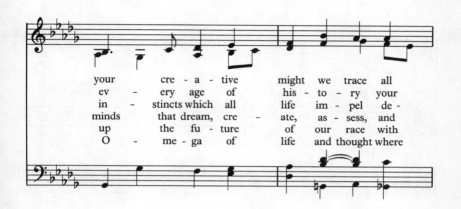

your   cre - a - tive   might   we   trace   all
ev - ery age   of   his - to - ry   your
in - stincts which all   life   im - pel   de -
minds   that dream, cre - ate,   as - sess,   and
up   the fu - ture   of   our   race   with
O - me - ga   of   life   and thought where

— Optional interlude between stanzas —

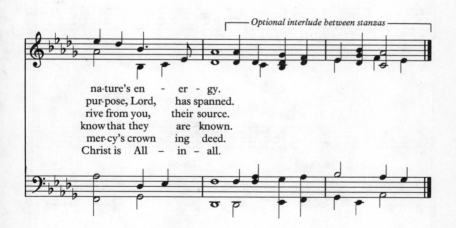

na-ture's en -   er - gy.
pur-pose, Lord,   has spanned.
rive from you,   their source.
know that they   are   known.
mer-cy's crown   ing   deed.
Christ is All — in — all.

WORDS: Albert F. Bayly and Brian Wren
MUSIC: Derek Williams

SAN ROCCO
CM

47

Lord Christ, the Father's Mighty Son

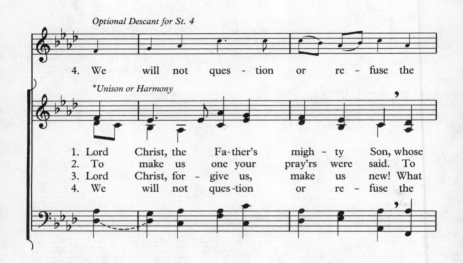

Optional Descant for St. 4

*Unison or Harmony

4. We will not ques - tion or re - fuse the

1. Lord Christ, the Fa-ther's migh - ty Son, whose
2. To make us one your pray'rs were said. To
3. Lord Christ, for - give us, make us new! What
4. We will not ques -tion or re - fuse the

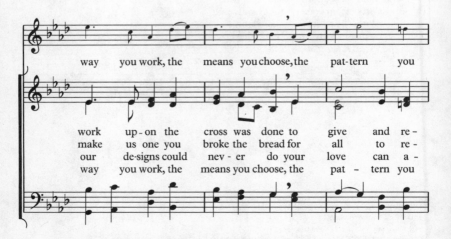

way you work, the means you choose, the pat-tern you

work up - on the cross was done to give and re -
make us one you broke the bread for all to re -
our de-signs could nev - er do your love can a -
way you work, the means you choose, the pat - tern you

*It is suggested that St. 2 be sung by a soloist or small group

weave, but re-con-cile our war-ring views

ceive, make all our scat-tered chur-ches one
ceive. Its piec-es scat-ter us in-stead:
chieve. Our pray'rs, our work, we bring to you
weave, but rec-on-cile our war-ring views

that the world may be - lieve.

that the world may be - lieve.
how can o - thers be - lieve?
that the world may be - lieve.
that the world may be - lieve.

WORDS: Brian Wren
MUSIC: John Wilson

EAST MEADS
88.5.8.6.

48 Let the Lord's People

1. Let the Lord's Peo - ple, heart and voice u -
2. This is the Lord's House, home of all his
3. This is the Lord's Day, day of God's own
4. In the Lord's Ser - vice bread and wine are

nit - ing, praise him who calls them out of sin and
peo - ple, school for the faith - ful, ref - uge for the
mak - ing, day of cre - a - tion, day of re - sur -
of - fered, that Christ may take them, bless them, break and

dark - ness in - to his own light, that he may cre -
sin - ner, rest for the pil - grim, hav - en for the
rec - tion, day of the Spir - it, Pen - te-cost re -
give them to all his peo - ple, his own life im -

ate them his ho - ly priest - hood.
wear - y; all find a wel - come.
peat - ed, day for re - joic - ing.
part - ing, food ev - er - last - ing.

WORDS: John Bowers
MUSIC: *Chartres Antiphoner*, 1784
    harm. John Wilson

AD TUUM NOMEN
11 11 11.5.

We Are Your People

49

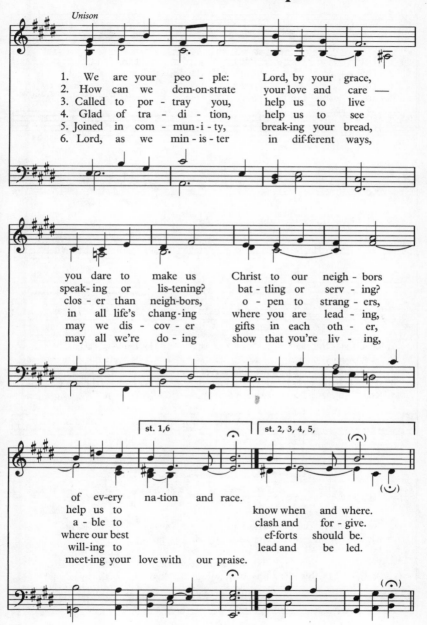

Unison

1. We are your peo - ple: Lord, by your grace,
2. How can we dem-on-strate your love and care —
3. Called to por - tray you, help us to live
4. Glad of tra - di - tion, help us to see
5. Joined in com - mun-i - ty, break-ing your bread,
6. Lord, as we min-is-ter in dif-ferent ways,

you dare to make us Christ to our neigh - bors
speak-ing or lis-tening? bat - tling or serv - ing?
clos - er than neigh-bors, o - pen to strang - ers,
in all life's chang-ing where you are lead - ing,
may we dis - cov - er gifts in each oth - er,
may all we're do - ing show that you're liv - ing,

st. 1,6   *st. 2, 3, 4, 5,*

of ev-ery na-tion and race.
help us to know when and where.
a - ble to clash and for - give.
where our best ef-forts should be.
will-ing to lead and be led.
meet-ing your love with our praise.

WORDS: Brian Wren
MUSIC: John Wilson
WHITFIELD
54. 557.

50 Jesu, Jesu, Fill Us with Your Love

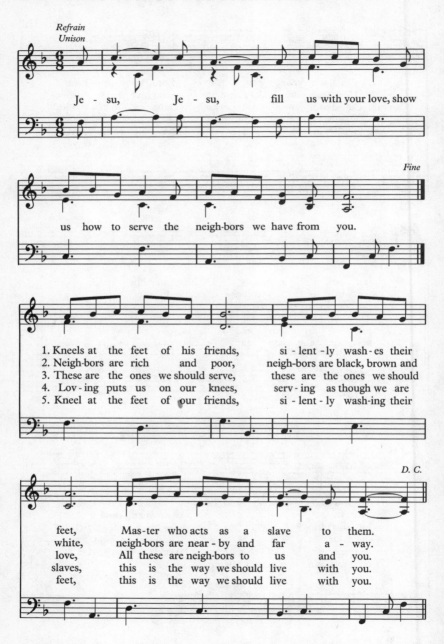

1. Kneels at the feet of his friends, si-lent-ly wash-es their
2. Neigh-bors are rich and poor, neigh-bors are black, brown and
3. These are the ones we should serve, these are the ones we should
4. Lov-ing puts us on our knees, serv-ing as though we are
5. Kneel at the feet of our friends, si-lent-ly wash-ing their

feet, Mas-ter who acts as a slave to them.
white, neigh-bors are near-by and far a-way.
love, All these are neigh-bors to us and you.
slaves, this is the way we should live with you.
feet, this is the way we should live with you.

WORDS: Tom Colvin
MUSIC: Ghana Folk Song, adapted by Tom Colvin, arr. by Jane Marshall

CHEREPONI
Irregular

Where Charity and Love Prevail 51

1. Where char - i - ty and love pre - vail
2. With grate - ful joy and ho - ly fear
3. For - give we now each oth - er's faults
4. Let strife a - mong us be un - known,
5. Let us re - call that in our midst

there God is ev - er found; brought here to - geth - er
his char - i - ty we learn; let us with heart and
as we our faults con - fess; and let us love each
let all con - ten - tion cease; be his the glo - ry
dwells God's be - got - ten Son; as mem - bers of his

by Christ's love by love are we thus bound.
mind and strength now love him in re - turn.
oth - er well in Chris - tian ho - li - ness.
that we seek, be ours his ho - ly peace.
Bo - dy joined we are in him made one.

6. Love can exclude no race or creed
   if honored be God's Name;
   our common life embraces all
   whose Father is the same.

WORDS: Latin; tr. Omer Westendorf
MUSIC: Melody and bass from *The Whole Booke of Psalmes*, 1592, alt.

CHESHIRE
CM

52 O Crucified Redeemer

1. O cru - ci - fied Re - deem - er, whose
2. We hear your cry of an - guish, we
3. The groan - ing of cre - a - tion wrung

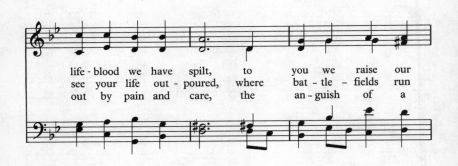

life - blood we have spilt, to you we raise our
see your life out - poured, where bat - tle - fields run
out by pain and care, the an - guish of a

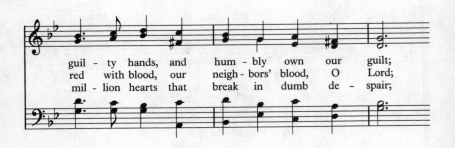

guil - ty hands, and hum - bly own our guilt;
red with blood, our neigh - bors' blood, O Lord;
mil - lion hearts that break in dumb de - spair;

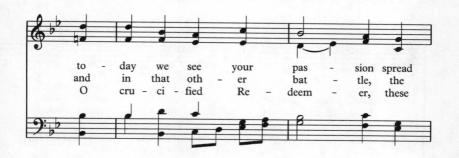

to - day we see your pas - sion spread
and in that oth - er bat - tle, the
O cru - ci - fied Re - deem - er, these

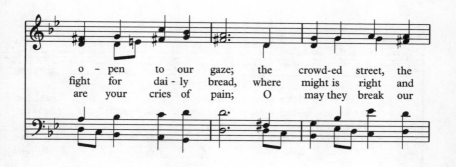

o - pen to our gaze; the crowd-ed street, the
fight for dai - ly bread, where might is right and
are your cries of pain; O may they break our

coun - try road, its Cal - va - ry dis - plays.
self is king, we see your thorn-crowned head.
self - ish hearts and love come in to reign.

WORDS: Timothy Rees   LLANGLOFFAN
MUSIC: Welsh Hymn Melody; harm. David Evans   76.86.D.

53
Lord, You Give the Great Commission

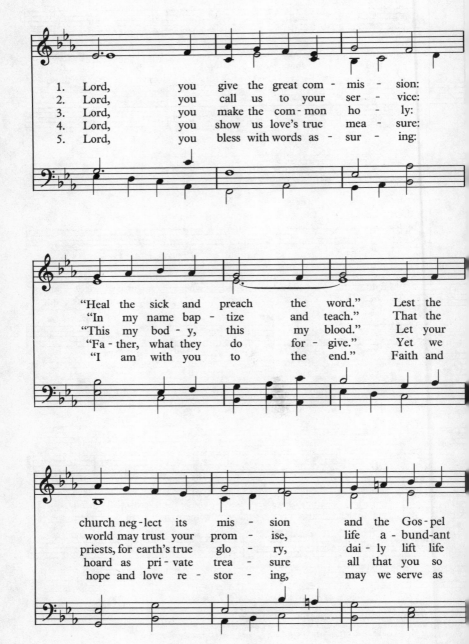

1. Lord, you give the great com - mis - sion:
2. Lord, you call us to your ser - vice:
3. Lord, you make the com - mon ho - ly:
4. Lord, you show us love's true mea - sure:
5. Lord, you bless with words as - sur - ing:

"Heal the sick and preach the word." Lest the
"In my name bap - tize and teach." That the
"This my bod - y, this my blood." Let your
"Fa - ther, what they do for - give." Yet we
"I am with you to the end." Faith and

church neg - lect its mis - sion and the Gos - pel
world may trust your prom - ise, life a - bund - ant
priests, for earth's true glo - ry, dai - ly lift life
hoard as pri - vate trea - sure all that you so
hope and love re - stor - ing, may we serve as

go un - heard, help us wit - ness to your
meant for each, give us all new fer - vor,
heav - en - ward, ask - ing that the world a -
free - ly give. May your care and mer - cy
you in - tend, and a - mid the cares that

pur - pose with re - newed in - teg - ri - ty;
draw us clos - er in com - mu - ni - ty;
round us share your chil-dren's lib - er - ty; with the
lead us to a just so - ci - e - ty;
claim us hold in mind e - ter - ni - ty;

Spir - it's gifts em - power us

for the work of min - is - try.

54

O Praise the Gracious Power

1. O praise the gra-cious power that tum - bles walls of
2. O praise per-sist - ent truth that o - pens fist - ed
3. O praise in - clu - sive love, en - cir - cling ev - ery
4. O praise the word of faith that claims us as God's
5. O praise the tide of grace that laps at ev - ery
6. O praise the power, the truth, the love, the word, the
7. O praise the liv - ing Christ with faith's bright song-ful

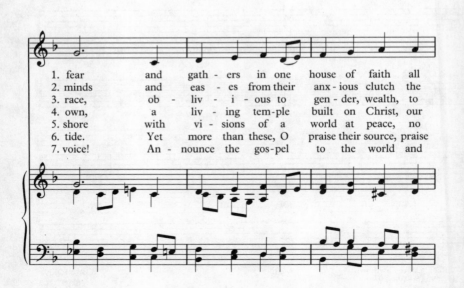

1. fear and gath - ers in one house of faith all
2. minds and eas - es from their anx - ious clutch the
3. race, ob - liv - i - ous to gen - der, wealth, to
4. own, a liv - ing tem-ple built on Christ, our
5. shore with vi - sions of a world at peace, no
6. tide. Yet more than these, O praise their source, praise
7. voice! An - nounce the gos-pel to the world and

1. stran - gers far and near:
2. prej - u - dice that blinds:
3. so - cial rank or place:
4. rock and cor - ner - stone:
5. long - er bled by war:
6. Christ the cru - ci - fied:
7. with these words re - joice:

We praise you,

Christ! Your cross has made us one!

WORDS: Thomas H. Troeger; Eph. 2:11-22
MUSIC: Carol Doran
Words and music used by permission of Oxford University Press.

CHRISTPRAISE RAY
SM with Refrain

55   Once on a Mountain Top

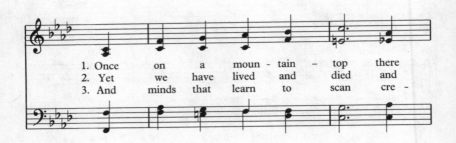

1. Once   on   a   moun - tain - top   there
2. Yet   we   have   lived   and   died   and
3. And   minds   that   learn   to   scan   cre -

stood   three   star - tled   men   who   saw   the   veil   of
found   of   God   no   trace. "Thou   art   a   God" (the
a - tion   like   a   book   say   noth - ing   lives   out -

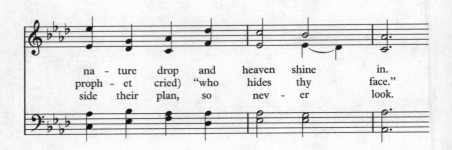

na - ture   drop   and   heaven   shine   in.
proph - et   cried)   "who   hides   thy   face."
side   their   plan,   so   nev - er   look.

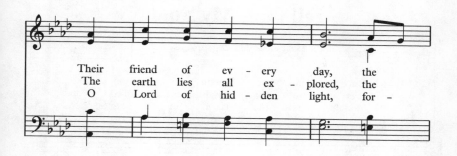

Their friend of ev – ery day, the
The earth lies all ex – plored, the
O Lord of hid – den light, for –

face they knew for his, they saw for one half –
heavens are ours to climb; and still no – one has
give us who des – pise the things which lie be –

hour the way he al – ways is.
seen our way God at an – y time.
yond our sight, and give us eyes.

WORDS: Michael Hewlett
MUSIC: Hebrew melody, arr: Meyer Lyon

LEONI
66. 84. D.

56

Tell Out, My Soul

Unison

1. Tell out, my soul, the great - ness of the
2. Tell out, my soul, the great - ness of his
3. Tell out, my soul, the great - ness of his
4. Tell out, my soul, the glo - ries of his

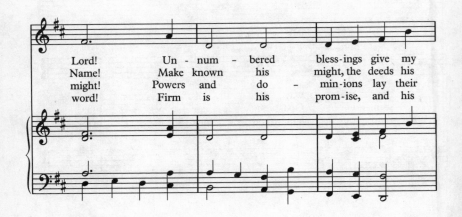

Lord!   Un - num - bered   bless-ings give my
Name!   Make known his   might, the deeds his
might!   Powers and do - min-ions lay their
word!   Firm is his   prom-ise, and his

WORDS: Timothy Dudley-Smith, Luke 1:46-55
MUSIC: Walter Greatorex

WOODLANDS
10 10.10 10.

57 The God Who Sent the Prophets

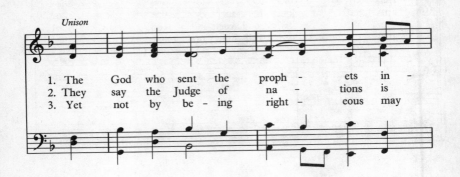

Unison

1. The God who sent the proph - ets in -
2. They say the Judge of na - tions is
3. Yet not by be - ing right - eous may

spired them for our good, to help us face the
mak - ing all things new; that when the man - y
we se - cure our place, or think to serve the

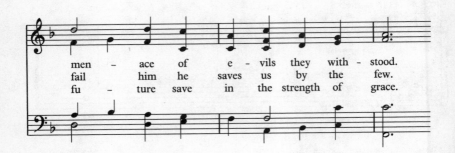

men - ace of e - vils they with - stood.
fail him he saves us by the few.
fu - ture save in the strength of grace.

How   faith - ful - ly they   warn   us,   from
In   this pro - phet - ic   prom - ise   our
For   there is   but   one   Sav - ior,   the

Is - rael's storm - y   past,   that   those who sow in –
anx - ious spir - its   rest: in   them, his cho - sen
One we   cru - ci – fied,   the   lone - ly Suf-fering

jus – tice   reap   judg - ment at   the   last!
Rem – nant,   the   fu – ture shall be   blest.
Ser – vant,   who   calls us   to   his   side.

WORDS: Fred Pratt Green   KING'S LYNN
MUSIC: English melody, arr. Ralph Vaughan Williams   76.76.D.

58
Thanks to God Whose Word

Unison

1. Thanks to God whose Word was spo - ken
2. Thanks to God whose Word In - car - nate
3. Thanks to God whose Word was writ - ten
4. Thanks to God whose Word is pub - lished
5. Thanks to God whose Word is ans - swered

in the deed that made the earth.
heights and depths of life did share.
in the Bi - ble's sa - cred page,
in the tongues of ev - ery race.
by the Spi - rit's voice with - in.

His the voice that called a na - tion;
Deeds and words and death and ris - ing,
re - cord of the rev - e - la - tion
See its glo - ry un - di - min - ished
Here we drink of joy un - meas - ured,

his   the   fires   that   tried   her   worth.
grace   in   hu - man   form   de - clare.
show - ing   God   to   ev - ery   age.
by   the   change   of   time   or   place.
life   re - deemed   from   death   and   sin.

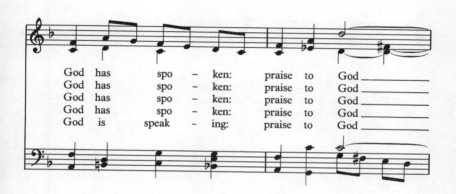

God has spo - ken: praise to God _____
God has spo - ken: praise to God _____
God has spo - ken: praise to God _____
God has spo - ken: praise to God _____
God is speak - ing: praise to God _____

_____ for the o - pen Word.
_____ for the o - pen Word.
_____ for the o - pen Word.
_____ for the o - pen Word.
_____ for the o - pen Word.

WORDS: R. T. Brooks
MUSIC: Peter Cutts

WYLDE GREEN
87.87. with Refrain

59

Eat This Bread

Ostinato Response

Eat this bread, drink this cup, come to me and nev - er be hun - gry. Eat this bread, drink this cup, trust in me and you will not thirst.

Eat this bread, drink this cup,

come to me and nev – er be hun – gry.

Eat this bread, drink this cup,

trust in me and you will not thirst.

Accompaniment
Keyboard or Guitar

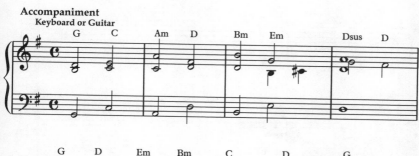

Verses (in this case, the response is not repeated as an ostinato; both the response and verses are sung one after the other)

Choir (humming) or Keyboard

Cantor

1. I am the bread of life, the

2. Your an-ces-tors ate man-na in the de-sert, but

3. Eat my flesh and drink my blood, and

4. An-y-one who eats this bread, will

5. If you be-lieve and eat this bread,

1. true bread sent from the Fa - ther.

2. this is the bread come down from heav - en.

3. I will raise you up on the last day.

4. live for - e - ver.

5. you will have e - ter - nal life.

*Choose either part

WORDS: John 6; adapted by Robert J. Batastini and the Taizé Community
MUSIC: Jacques Berthier

60 These Things Did Thomas Count

1. These things did Thomas count as real:
2. The vi - sion of his skep - tic mind
3. His rea - soned cer - tain - ties de - nied
4. May we, O God, by grace be - lieve

the warmth of blood, the chill of steel,
was keen e - nough to make him blind
that one could live when one had died,
and thus the ris - en Christ re - ceive,

the grain of wood, the heft of stone,
to an - y un - ex - pect - ed act
un - til his fin - gers read like Braille
whose raw, im - print - ed palms reached out

the last frail twitch of flesh and bone.
too large for his small world of fact.
the mark - ings of the spear and nail.
and beck - oned Thom - as from his doubt.

WORDS: Thomas H. Troeger; John 20:19-31.
MUSIC: Carol Doran
Words and music used by permission of Oxford University Press.

MERLE MARIE
LM

We Who Once Were Dead

61

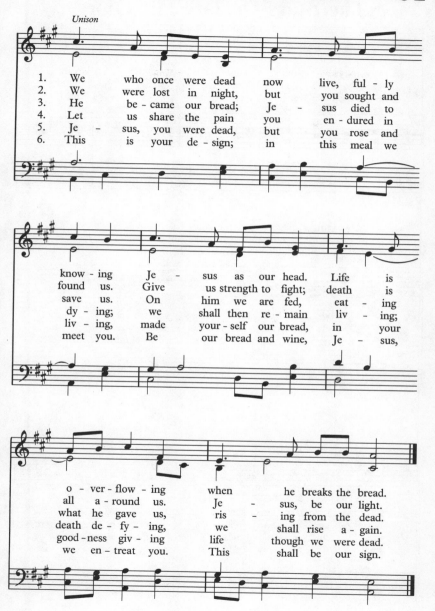

Unison

1. We who once were dead now live, ful - ly
2. We were lost in night, but you sought and
3. He be - came our bread; Je - sus died to
4. Let us share the pain you en - dured in
5. Je - sus, you were dead, but you rose and
6. This is your de - sign; in this meal we

know - ing Je - sus as our head. Life is
found us. Give us strength to fight; death is
save us. On him we are fed, eat - ing
dy - ing; we shall then re - main liv - ing;
liv - ing, made your - self our bread, in your
meet you. Be our bread and wine, Je - sus,

o - ver - flow - ing when he breaks the bread.
all a - round us. Je - sus, be our light.
what he gave us, ris - ing from the dead.
death de - fy - ing, we shall rise a - gain.
good - ness giv - ing life though we were dead.
we en - treat you. This shall be our sign.

WORDS: Muus Jacobse, tr. composite
MUSIC: Rik Veelenturf

MIDDEN IN DE DOOD
565.65.

62

The Stars Declare His Glory

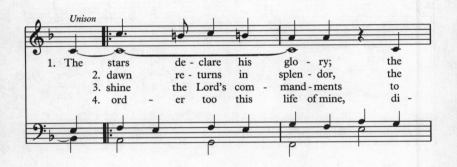

1. The stars   de - clare his   glo - ry;   the
2. dawn   re - turns in   splen - dor,   the
3. shine   the Lord's com -   mand - ments   to
4. ord -   er too this   life of mine,   di -

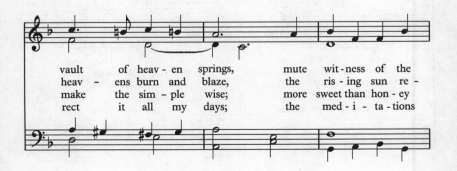

vault   of heav - en springs,   mute wit - ness of the
heav -   ens burn and blaze,   the ris - ing sun re -
make   the sim - ple wise;   more sweet than hon - ey
rect   it all my days;   the med - i - ta - tions

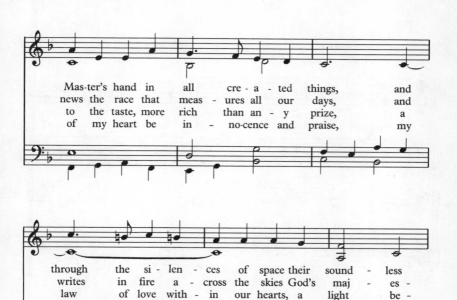

Mas-ter's hand in all cre - a - ted things, and
news the race that meas - ures all our days, and
to the taste, more rich than an - y prize, a
of my heart be in - no-cence and praise, my

through the si - len - ces of space their sound - less
writes in fire a - cross the skies God's maj - es -
law of love with - in our hearts, a light be -
Rock, and my re - deem-ing Lord, in all my

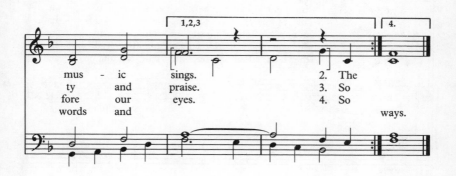

1,2,3   4.

mus - ic sings.
ty and praise.   2. The
fore our eyes.   3. So
words and   4. So   ways.

WORDS: Timothy Dudley-Smith; based on Psalm 19
MUSIC: Alec Wyton

PSALM 19
87. 86. 86.

63

The Voice of God

1. The voice of God goes out to all the
2. The Lord has said: "Re - ceive my mes - sen -
3. The bro - ken reed he will not tram - ple
4. A - noint - ed with the Spir - it and with
5. His touch will bless the eyes that dark - ness

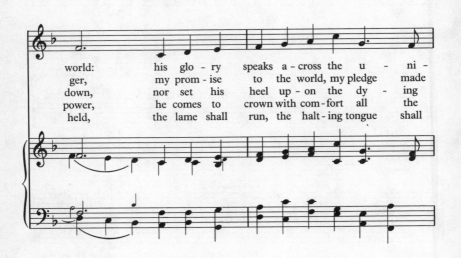

world: his glo - ry speaks a - cross the u - ni -
ger, my prom - ise to the world, my pledge made
down, nor set his heel up - on the dy - ing
power, he comes to crown with com - fort all the
held, the lame shall run, the halt - ing tongue shall

WORDS: 'Peter Icarus' (Luke Connaughton)
MUSIC: George Dyson

WINTON
10 10.10 10.

64

There's a Spirit in the Air

Unison

1. There's a spir - it in the air,
2. Lose your shy - ness, find your tongue,
3. When be - liev - ers break the bread,
4. Still the Spir - it gives us light,
5. When a strang - er's not a - lone,

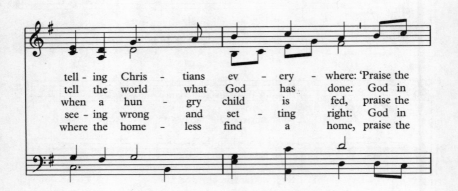

tell - ing Chris - tians ev - ery - where: 'Praise the
tell the world what God has done: God in
when a hun - gry child is fed, praise the
see - ing wrong and set - ting right: God in
where the home - less find a home, praise the

love   that   Christ   re - vealed,   liv -
Christ   has   come   to   stay.   Live
love   that   Christ   re - vealed,   liv -
Christ   has   come   to   stay.   Live
love   that   Christ   re - vealed,   liv -

ing,   work - ing   in   our   world.'
to - mor - row's   life   to - day!
ing,   work - ing   in   our   world.
to - mor - row's   life   to - day!
ing,   work - ing   in   our   world.

6. May the Spirit fill our praise,
   guide our thoughts and change our ways.
   God in Christ has come to stay.
   Live tomorrow's life today!

7. There's a Spirit in the air,
   calling people everywhere;
   praise the love that Christ revealed:
   living, working in our world.

WORDS: Brian Wren
MUSIC: William P. Rowan
Words Copyright © 1979 by Hope Publishing Company, Carol Stream, IL 60188.
Music Copyright © 1987 by Hope Publishing Company. All Rights Reserved.

FREINER
77.77.

65
This Is a Day of New Beginnings

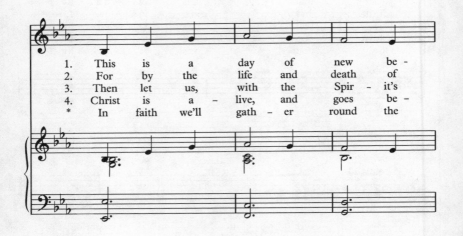

1. This is a day of new be -
2. For by the life and death of
3. Then let us, with the Spir - it's
4. Christ is a - live, and goes be -
* In faith we'll gath - er round the

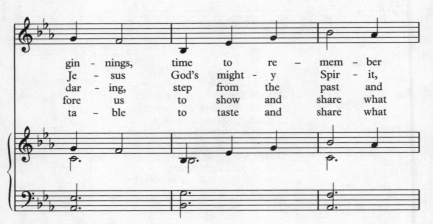

gin - nings, time to re - mem - ber
Je - sus God's might - y Spir - it,
dar - ing, step from the past and
fore us to show and share what
ta - ble to taste and share what

*Alternate text for Holy Communion

and move on, time to be - lieve what
now as then, can make for us a
leave be - hind our dis - ap - point - ment,
love can do. This is a day of
love can do. This is a day of

love is bring - ing, lay - ing to
world of dif - ference, as faith and
guilt and griev - ing, seek - ing new
new be - gin - nings — our God is
new be - gin - nings — our God is

1,2,3 **4.**

rest the pain that's gone.
hope are born a - gain.
paths, and sure to find.
mak - ing all things 4. new.
mak - ing all things 5. new.

WORDS: Brian Wren, alt.
MUSIC: Carlton R. Young

BEGINNINGS
98. 98.

66 Your Heart, O God, Is Grieved

Solo/Soli

1. O God, Father in heav - en, have mer-cy up - on us.
2. O Son of God, redeemer of the world, have mer-cy up - on us.
3. O God, Holy Spir - it, have mer-cy up - on us.

All

Your heart, O God is grieved, we know, by ev - ery
Your arms ex - tend, O Christ, to save from sting of
O lav - ish Giv - er, come to aid the chil - dren

e - vil, ev - ery woe; up - on your cross - for -
death and grasp of grave; your scars be - fore the
that your word has made; now make us grow and

sak - en Son our death is laid, and peace is won.
Fa - ther move his heart to mer - cy at such love.
help us pray; bring joy and com - fort; come to stay.

WORDS: Jiři Tranovský, 1636, tr. Jaroslav J. Vajda
MUSIC: Škultéty, Partitura, 1798

ZNÁME TO, PANE BOŽE NÁS
Irregular

O Christ, the Healer

1. O Christ, the heal - er, we have come to pray for health, to plead for friends. How can we fail to be re - stored when reached by love that nev - er ends?

2. From ev - ery ail - ment flesh en - dures our bod - ies clam - or to be freed; yet in our hearts we would con - fess that whole - ness is our deep - est need.

3. In con - flicts that de - stroy our health we rec - og - nize the world's dis - ease; our com - mon life de - clares our ills. Is there no cure, O Christ, for these?

4. Grant that we all, made one in faith, in your com - mu - ni - ty may find the whole - ness that, en - rich - ing us, shall reach and pros - per hu - man - kind.

WORDS: Fred Pratt Green
MUSIC: William Knapp

WAREHAM
LM

68

This Is the Feast

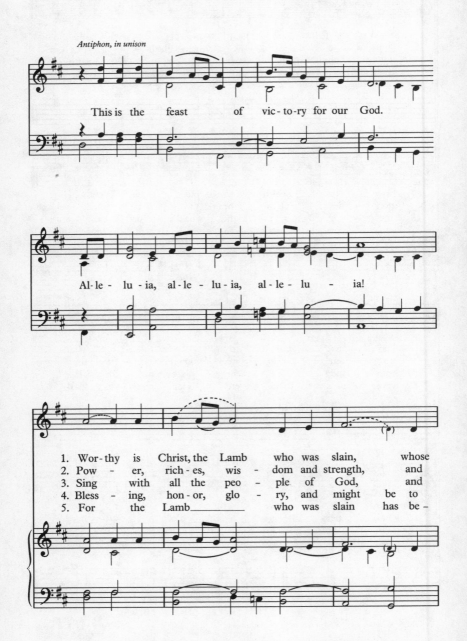

Antiphon, in unison

This is the feast of vic-to-ry for our God.

Al - le - lu - ia, al - le - lu - ia, al - le - lu - ia!

1. Wor-thy is Christ, the Lamb who was slain, whose
2. Pow - er, rich - es, wis - dom and strength, and
3. Sing with all the peo - ple of God, and
4. Bless - ing, hon - or, glo - ry, and might be to
5. For the Lamb who was slain has be -

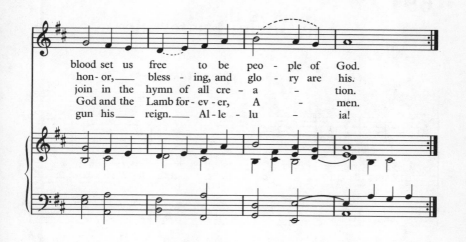

blood set us free to be peo - ple of God.
hon - or,___ bless - ing, and glo - ry are his.
join in the hymn of all cre - a - tion.
God and the Lamb for - ev - er, A - men.
gun his___ reign.___ Al - le - lu - ia!

Final Antiphon

This is the feast of vic - to - ry for our God.

Al - le - lu - ia, al - le - lu - ia, al - le - lu - ia!

WORDS: Revelation 5:12-13; adap. John W. Arthur
MUSIC: Richard Hillert
Music Copyright © 1975, Richard Hillert.

FESTIVAL CANTICLE
Irreg. with Refrain

69

This Joyful Eastertide

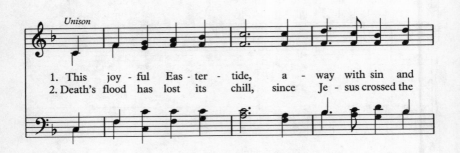

1. This joy - ful Eas - ter - tide, a - way with sin and
2. Death's flood has lost its chill, since Je - sus crossed the

sor - row! My love, the Cru - ci - fied, has
riv - er: Lov - er of souls, from ill my

sprung to life this mor - row.
pass - ing soul de - liv - er.

Had Christ, who once was slain, ne'er burst his three-day pris-
on, our faith had been in vain; but
now has Christ a - ris - en, a - ris - en, a -
ris - en, a - ris - en!

WORDS: George R. Woodward; Mark 16:6
MUSIC: Dutch, 17th cent.; arr. Alice Parker
Harm. Copyright ©1969, by Alice Parker. Assigned 1987 to Hope Publishing Company. All Rights Reserved.

VRUECHTEN
Irregular

70 There's a Wideness in God's Mercy

Introduction

Descant for flute or violin (last time only)

1. There's a wide-ness   in God's mer - cy like the wide-ness
2. There is no place where earth's sor - rows are more felt than
3. For the love of   God is   broad - er than the meas-ure

  of   the sea;   there's a kind - ness in his   jus -
  up   in heaven;   there is no place where earth's fail -
  of   the mind;   and the heart of   the E - ter -

tice, which is more than lib - er - ty.
ings have such kind-ly judg-ment given.
nal is most won-der - ful - ly kind.

There is wel-come
There is plen - ti -
If our love were

for the sin - ner,
ful re - demp - tion
but more faith - ful,

and more grac - es for the
in the blood that has been
we should take him at his

good; there is mer - cy
shed; there is joy for
word; and our life would

with the Sa - vior;
all the mem - bers
be thanks-giv - ing

there is heal·ing in his blood.
in the sor·rows of the Head.
for the good·ness of the Lord.

Interlude/Conclusion

*Descant instrument may play this interlude each time.

WORDS: Frederick William Faber, alt.
MUSIC: Calvin Hampton

ST. HELENA
87. 87. D

The Kingdom of God

1. The king-dom of God is like a grain of mus-tard seed.
2. For when it is sown, it grows in-to the larg-est plant,
3. It grows so birds can rest in-side its crown of leaves,
4. And so we can lik-en it to seeds which make a tree

When it is sown in the earth it is the small-est seed.
great-er than all of the herbs and grows in-to a tree.
deep in its shad-ows a-way from an-y e-vil prey.
larg-er than all of the trees from just the small-est seed.

It is like the king-dom of God and a mys-ter-y.
It is like the king-dom of God and a mys-ter-y.
It is like the king-dom of God and a mys-ter-y.
It is like the king-dom of God and a mys-ter-y.

WORDS: Gracia Grindal, Mark 4:30-34
MUSIC: Austin C. Lovelace

MUSTARD SEED
76.76.85.

72 We Know that Christ Is Raised

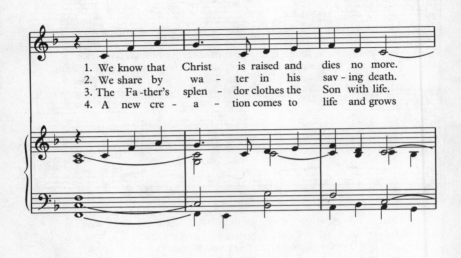

1. We know that Christ is raised and dies no more.
2. We share by wa - ter in his sav - ing death.
3. The Fa - ther's splen - dor clothes the Son with life.
4. A new cre - a - tion comes to life and grows

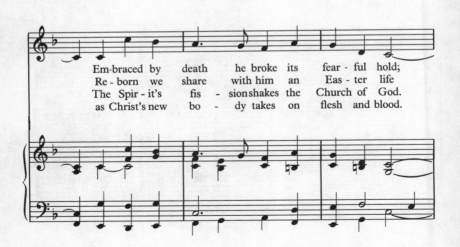

Em-braced by death he broke its fear - ful hold;
Re - born we share with him an Eas - ter life
The Spir - it's fis - sion shakes the Church of God.
as Christ's new bo - dy takes on flesh and blood.

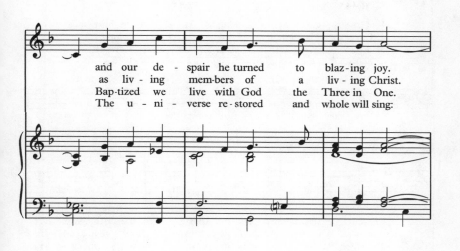

and our de - spair he turned to blaz-ing joy.
as liv - ing mem-bers of a liv - ing Christ.
Bap-tized we live with God the Three in One.
The u - ni - verse re-stored and whole will sing:

1-3

Al - le - lu - ia!

Final Ending

lu - ia!

WORDS: John Brownlow Geyer
MUSIC: Charles Villiers Stanford
Words used by permission of John Geyer.

ENGELBERG
10 10 10. with Alleluia

73   Gracious Spirit, Holy Ghost

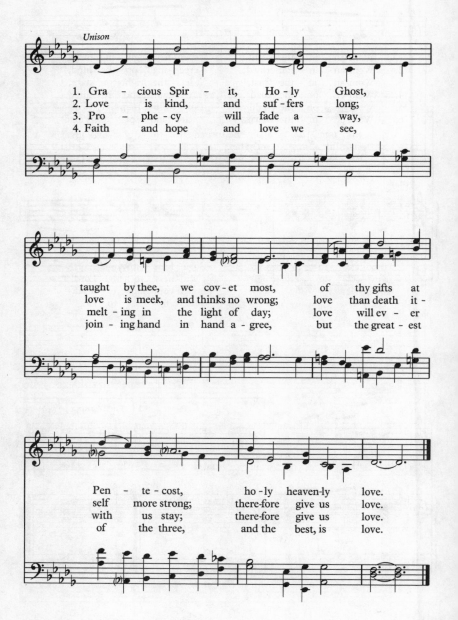

Unison

1. Gra - cious Spir - it, Ho - ly Ghost,
2. Love is kind, and suf -fers long;
3. Pro - phe -cy will fade a - way,
4. Faith and hope and love we see,

taught by thee, we cov-et most, of thy gifts at
love is meek, and thinks no wrong; love than death it -
melt - ing in the light of day; love will ev - er
join - ing hand in hand a - gree, but the great - est

Pen - te -cost, ho -ly heaven-ly love.
self more strong; there-fore give us love.
with us stay; there-fore give us love.
of the three, and the best, is love.

WORDS: Christopher Wordsworth
MUSIC: Jane Marshall

ANDERSON
77.75.

Woman in the Night

74

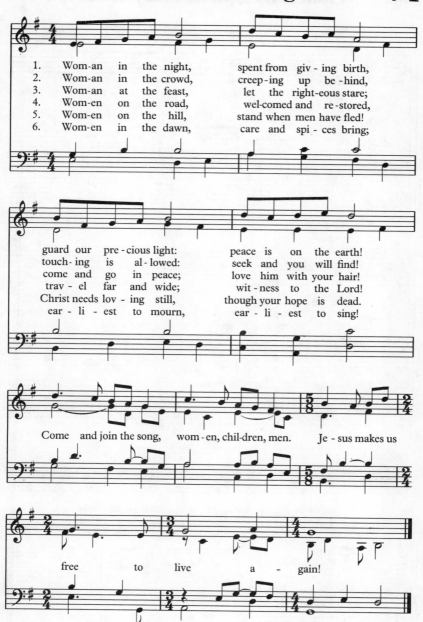

1. Wom-an in the night, spent from giv-ing birth,
2. Wom-an in the crowd, creep-ing up be-hind,
3. Wom-an at the feast, let the right-eous stare;
4. Wom-en on the road, wel-comed and re-stored,
5. Wom-en on the hill, stand when men have fled!
6. Wom-en in the dawn, care and spi-ces bring;

guard our pre-cious light: peace is on the earth!
touch-ing is al-lowed: seek and you will find!
come and go in peace; love him with your hair!
trav-el far and wide; wit-ness to the Lord!
Christ needs lov-ing still, though your hope is dead.
ear-li-est to mourn, ear-li-est to sing!

Come and join the song, wom-en, chil-dren, men. Je-sus makes us

free to live a - gain!

WORDS: Brian Wren
MUSIC: Jane Marshall

NOEL NEW
10.10. with Refrain

75 Wind Who Makes All Winds

1. Wind who makes all winds that blow—
2. Fire who fuels all fires that burn—
3. Ho - ly Spir - it, Wind and Flame,

gusts that bend the sap-lings low, gales that heave the
suns a-round which plan-ets turn, bea - cons mark-ing
move with-in our mor-tal frame, make our hearts an

sea in waves, stir-rings in the mind's deep caves —
reefs and shoals, shin-ing truth to guide our souls —
al - tar pyre, kin - dle them with your own fire.

aim your breath with stead-y power on your
come to us as once you came: burst in
Breathe and blow up-on that blaze 'til our

church, this day, this hour. Raise, re-new the
tongues of sa-cred flame! Light and Pow-er,
lives, our deeds and ways speak that tongue which

ritard.

life we've lost, Spir-it God of Pen-te-cost.
Might and Strength, fill your church, its breadth and length.
ev-ery land by your grace shall un-der-stand.

ritard.

WORDS: Thomas H. Troeger, Acts 2:1 - 13
MUSIC: Carol Doran
Words ©1983, Thomas H. Troeger.
Music ©1985, Oxford University Press, Inc. Used by permission of the publisher.

FALCONE
77.77.D.

76   For the Fruit of All Creation

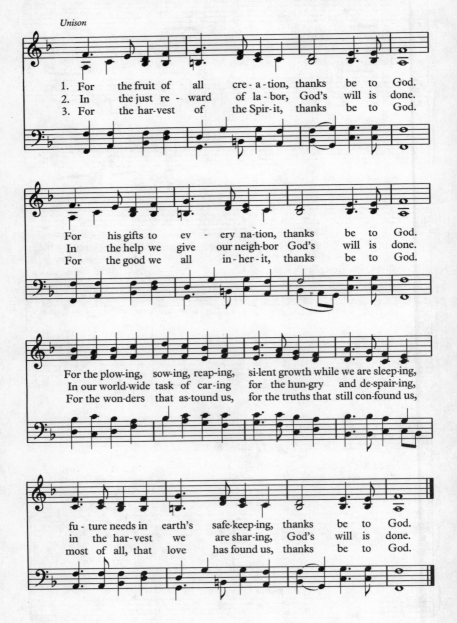

Unison

1. For the fruit of all cre - a -tion, thanks be to God.
2. In the just re - ward of la - bor, God's will is done.
3. For the har-vest of the Spir-it, thanks be to God.

For his gifts to ev - ery na-tion, thanks be to God.
In the help we give our neigh-bor God's will is done.
For the good we all in - her - it, thanks be to God.

For the plow-ing, sow-ing, reap-ing, si-lent growth while we are sleep-ing,
In our world-wide task of car-ing, for the hun-gry and de-spair-ing,
For the won-ders that as-tound us, for the truths that still con-found us,

fu - ture needs in earth's safe-keep-ing, thanks be to God.
in the har-vest we are shar-ing, God's will is done.
most of all, that love has found us, thanks be to God.

WORDS: Fred Pratt Green
MUSIC: Trad. Welsh Melody, harm L.O. Emerson

AR HYD Y NOS
84.84.888.4.

What Gift Can We Bring

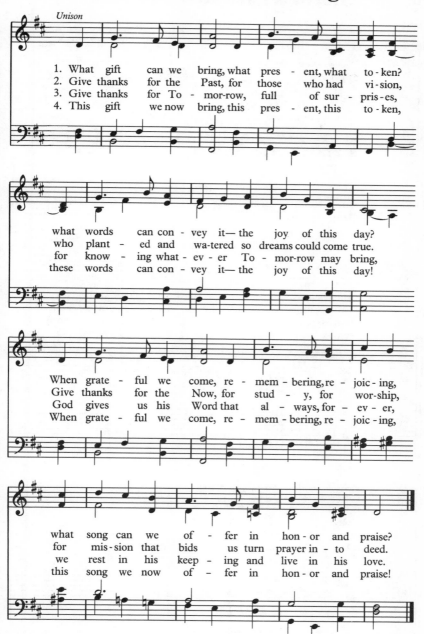

WORDS and MUSIC: Jane Marshall

ANNIVERSARY SONG
11 11. 11 11.

78
Lord, As We Rise to Leave

1. Lord, as we rise to leave this shell of wor - ship, called to the risk of un - pro - tec - ted liv - ing,
2. For all the strain with liv - ing in - ter - wo - ven, for the de - mands each day will make up - on us,
3. Give us an eye for o - pen - ings to serve you; make us a - lert when calm is in - ter - rupt - ed,
4. Lift from our life the blan - ket of con - ven - tion: give us the nerve to lose our life to oth - ers.

will – ing to be at one with all your
and for the love we owe the mod – ern
rea – dy and wise to use the un – ex –
Be with your church in death and res – ur –

1-3.

peo – ple, we ask for cour - age.
cit – y, Lord, make us cheer-ful.
pec – ted; shar – pen our in - sight.

4.

rec – tion: Lord of all a – ges.

WORDS: Fred Kaan
MUSIC: Erik Routley

WANSBECK
11 11 11.5.

79 Sent Forth by God's Blessing

1. Sent forth by God's bless-ing, our true faith con - fess-ing, the
2. With praise and thanks - giv-ing to God ev - er - liv-ing, the

peo - ple of God from his dwell - ing take leave.
tasks of our ev - ery - day life we will face.

The sup - per is end-ed. Oh, now be ex - tend-ed the
Our faith ev - er shar-ing, in love ev - er car-ing, em -

fruits of this ser - vice in all who be - lieve. The
brac - ing his chil - dren of each tribe and race. With

seed of his teach-ing, re - cep - tive souls reach-ing, shall
your feast you feed us, with your light now lead us; u -

blos - som in ac - tion for God and for all. His
nite us as one in this life that we share. Then

grace did in - vite us, his love shall u - nite us to
may all the liv - ing with praise and thanks - giv-ing give

work for God's king - dom and an -swer his call.
hon - or to Christ and his name that we bear.

WORDS: Omer Westendorf
MUSIC: Welsh folk tune

THE ASH GROVE
6 6 11. 6 6 11.D.

Words Copyright © 1964, World Library Publications, Inc. All Rights Reserved. Used by permission.
Setting Copyright © 1972 CONTEMPORARY WORSHIP 4: Hymns for Baptism and Holy Communion. Used by permission of
Augsburg Publishing House.

80

Then the Glory

♩. = c. 60
Unison

Then the glo - ry Then the rest Then the sab - bath peace un -

brok - en Then the gar - den Then the throne Then the crys - tal

riv - er flow - ing Then the splen - dor Then the life

Then the new cre - a - tion sing - ing

Then the mar-riage Then the love Then the feast of
joy un-end-ing Then the know-ing Then the light
Then the ul-ti-mate ad-ven-ture Then the Spir-it's
har-vest gath-ered Then the Lamb in maj-es-ty
Then the Fa-ther's A-men Then Then Then.

WORDS: Jaroslav J. Vajda
MUSIC: Carl F. Schalk

NOW
Irregular

81

Two-Stanza Introits for the
Chief Festivals of the Christian Year

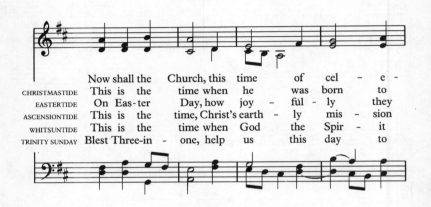

	Now shall the	Church, this	time		of	cel –	e –
CHRISTMASTIDE	This is the	time when	he		was	born	to
EASTERTIDE	On Eas-ter	Day, how	joy –		ful –	ly	they
ASCENSIONTIDE	This is the	time, Christ's earth –			ly	mis –	sion
WHITSUNTIDE	This is the	time when	God		the	Spir –	it
TRINITY SUNDAY	Blest Three-in –	one, help	us		this	day	to

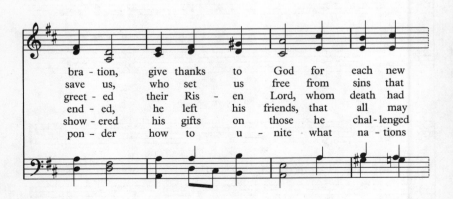

bra – tion,	give thanks	to	God	for	each	new
save us,	who set	us	free	from	sins	that
greet – ed	their Ris –	en	Lord,	whom	death	had
end – ed,	he left	his	friends,	that	all	may
show – ered	his gifts	on	those	he	chal – lenged
pon – der	how to	u –	nite	what	na – tions

rev - e - la - tion, for gos - pel
would en - slave us; for Ma - ry's
not de - feat - ed. What he be -
be be - friend - ed: so close he
and em - pow - ered. See how the
put a - sun - der; deep - en our

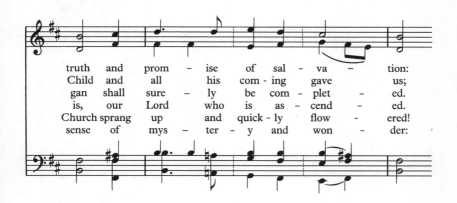

truth and prom - ise of sal - va - tion:
Child and all his com - ing gave us;
gan shall sure - ly be com - plet - ed.
is, our Lord who is as - cend - ed.
Church sprang up and quick - ly flow - ered!
sense of mys - ter - y and won - der:

To God be end - less praise!

WORDS: Fred Pratt Green
MUSIC: From the four-part chorale (BWV 400), J.S. Bach

O HERZENSANGST
11 11 11. 6.

82 It Is God Who Holds the Nations

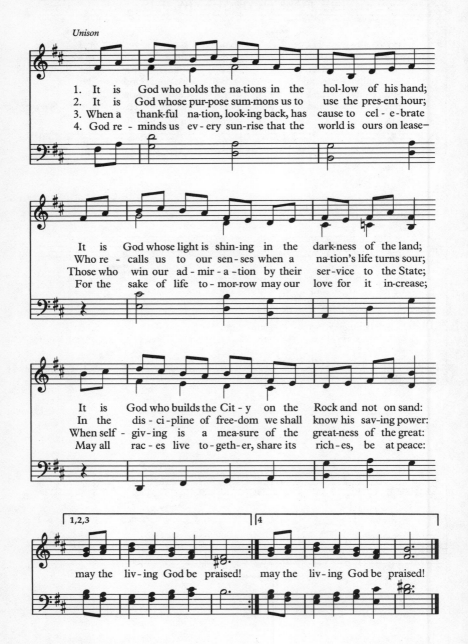

Unison

1. It is God who holds the na-tions in the hol-low of his hand;
2. It is God whose pur-pose sum-mons us to use the pres-ent hour;
3. When a thank-ful na-tion, look-ing back, has cause to cel - e-brate
4. God re - minds us ev - ery sun-rise that the world is ours on lease—

It is God whose light is shin-ing in the dark-ness of the land;
Who re - calls us to our sen - ses when a na-tion's life turns sour;
Those who win our ad - mir - a -tion by their ser-vice to the State;
For the sake of life to - mor-row may our love for it in-crease;

It is God who builds the Cit - y on the Rock and not on sand:
In the dis - ci -pline of free-dom we shall know his sav-ing power:
When self - giv-ing is a mea-sure of the great-ness of the great:
May all rac - es live to-geth-er, share its rich - es, be at peace:

1,2,3 may the liv - ing God be praised! **4** may the liv - ing God be praised!

WORDS: Fred Pratt Green
MUSIC: Austin C. Lovelace

HERITAGE
15 15 15.7.

INDEX OF COPYRIGHT OWNERS

BINGDON PRESS, 201 Eighth Avenue, South, P. O. Box 801, Nashville, TN 37202—(615) 749-6422: Hymn 44.

RCHDIOCESAN MUSIC OFFICE, 222 N. Seventeenth Street, Philadelphia, PA 19103—(215) 587-3696: Hymn 43.

UGSBURG PUBLISHING HOUSE, 426 S. Fifth Street, Box 1209, Minneapolis, MN 55440—(612) 330-3300: Hymns 7, 18, 21, 35, 61, 68, 79.

OWERS, CANON JOHN E., The Vicarage, Ashby-de-la-Zouch, Leicestershire, LE6, 5BX, England—412180 (STD 0530): Hymn 48.

ROADMAN PRESS, 127 Ninth Avenue North, Nashville, TN 37234—(615) 251-2000: Hymn 40.

OLUMBIA PICTURES PUBLICATIONS, 15800 N. W. 48th Avenue, P. O. Box 4340, Miami, FL 33014-9969—(305) 620-1500: Hymn 12.

OMMUNITY OF THE RESURRECTION, Mirfield, West Yorkshire, WF14 OBN, England—(0924) 493272: Hymn 52.

ONCORDIA PUBLISHING HOUSE, 3558 S. Jefferson Ave., St. Louis, MO 63118—(314) 664-7000: Hymns 11, 17.

VANS, C. W. A., 13 Cheyham Way, Cheam, Surrey, SM2 7HX, England: Hymn 22.

XECUTORS OF THE ESTATE OF BASIL HARWOOD, The Public Trustee, Stewart House, Kingsway, London, WC2B 6JX, England—01-405 4300: Hymn 20.

ALAXY MUSIC CORPORATION, 131 West 86th St., New York, NY 10024—(212) 874-2100: Hymn 55.

ERIKE, HENRY V., Concordia Seminary, 801 DeMun Ave., St. Louis, MO 63105: Hymn 35.

EYER, JOHN, 5 Weoley Hill, Birmingham, B29 4AA, England: Hymn 72.

. I. A. PUBLICATIONS, INC. 7404 S. Mason Ave., Chicago, IL 60638—(312) 496-3800: Hymns 4, 6, 14, 22, 23, 24, 59, 70.

OOI & STICHT, Vaartweg 51, Postbus 17, 1200 aa Hilversum, The Netherlands: Hymn 61.

ARCOURT BRACE JOVANOVICH, INC., Orlando, FL 32887—(305) 345-2000: Hymn 24.

ILLERT, RICHARD, 1620 Clay Court, Melrose Park, IL 60160: Hymn 68.

INSHAW MUSIC, INC., P. O. Box 470, Chapel Hill, NC 27514—(919) 933-1691: Hymns 2, 36.

OPE PUBLISHING COMPANY, Carol Stream, IL 60188—(312) 665-3200: Hymns 1, 4, 8, 9, 10, 12, 13, 14, 16, 19, 20, 23, 27, 28, 29, 30, 31, 32, 33, 34, 37, 39, 41, 42, 45, 46, 47, 48, 49, 50, 53, 56, 57, 58, 62, 64, 65, 67, 69, 71, 73, 74, 76, 77, 78, 80, 81, 82.

INDEX OF COPYRIGHT OWNERS

HYMN SOCIETY OF AMERICA, THE (contact HOPE PUBLISHING COMPANY): Hymns 25, 40.

HYMNS ANCIENT & MODERN LIMITED, St. Mary's Works, St. Mary's Plain, Norwich, No folk, NR3 3BH, England—(0603) 612914: Hymn 36.

JEFFERYS, JR., ROBERT F., Flex-Flow Company, 375 Weadley Road, King of Prussia, PA 19406—(215) 688-8511: Hymn 44.

LeCROY, ANNE K., Box 22, 990A, ETSU, Johnson City, TN 37614: Hymn 6.

LUTHERAN WORLD FEDERATION, THE, P. O. Box No. 66, Route de Ferney 150, 12 Geneva 20, Switzerland—91 61 11: Hymns 21, 66.

McCRIMMON PUBLISHING CO. LTD., 10-12 High Street, Great Wakering, Essex, SS3 OE England—(0702) 218956: Hymn 63.

NOVELLO & COMPANY LTD., Borough Green, Sevenoaks, Kent, TN15 8DT, England 883261: Hymn 63.

OXFORD UNIVERSITY PRESS, 200 Madison Avenue, New York, NY 10016—(212) 679-730 Hymns 5, 54, 60, 75.

OXFORD UNIVERSITY PRESS, Ely House, 37 Dover Street, London, W1X 4AH, England 01-493 2661: Hymns 10, 46, 52, 56, 57.

PEACEY, MRS. M. E., 10 Park Cottages, Manor Road, Hurstpierpoint, West Sussex, BN6 9U England: Hymn 42.

PETERSON, MICHAEL L., Zion Lutheran Church, 1254 S. Lincoln Street, Shawano, W 54166—(715) 526-2017: Hymn 31.

ROWTHORN, JEFFERY W., Institute of Sacred Music, Yale University, 409 Prospect Stre New Haven, CT 06510—(203) 436-2915: Hymn 53.

SCHALK, DR. CARL, Concordia College, 7400 Augusta Street, River Forest, IL 60305-1499 (312) 771-8300: Hymns 26, 38.

SHORE, J. W., 158 Hilltop Drive, Kirkholt, Rochdale, Lancashire, OL11 2RZ, Englar Hymn 15.

VAJDA, JAROSLAV J., 9839 Briarstone Drive, St. Louis, MO 63126: Hymns 26, 38.

WILLIAMS, DEREK, 86 Richmond Road, Cambridge, CB4 3PT, England: Hymn 46.

WORLD LIBRARY PUBLICATIONS, INC., 3815 N. Willow Road, Schiller Park, IL 6017((312) 678-0621: Hymns 51, 79.

METRICAL INDEX

METRICAL INDEX

10 11 11.6.
Christe Sanctorum, 34

11 11 11.5.
Ad Tuum Nomen, 48
Mighty Savior, 6
Wansbeck, 78
Wojtkiewiecz, 18

11 11 11.6.
O Herzensangst, 81

11 11.11 11.
Anniversary Song, 77

12 9.12 9. with Refrain
Natomah, 30

15 15 15.7.
Heritage, 82

Irregular
Carpenter, 17
Chereponi, 50
Ghana, 9
Granton, 7
Marvel, 26
Now, 33, 80
Vruechten, 69
Známe To, Pane Bože Nás, 66

Irregular with Refrain
Festival Canticle, 68

TUNE NAME INDEX

AUTHORS, COMPOSERS AND SOURCES INDEX

AUTHORS, COMPOSERS AND SOURCES INDEX

AUTHORS, COMPOSERS AND SOURCES INDEX

TOPICAL AND LITURGICAL INDEX

TOPICAL AND LITURGICAL INDEX

TOPICAL AND LITURGICAL INDEX

ALPHABETICAL INDEX OF HYMNS

ALPHABETICAL INDEX OF HYMNS